The photosynthesis
of carbon compounds

The

Photosynthesis of

Carbon Compounds

Melvin Calvin

J. A. Bassham

&

University of California
Berkeley, California

W. A. Benjamin, Inc.   New York   1962

THE PHOTOSYNTHESIS OF CARBON COMPOUNDS

Library of Congress Catalog Card Number: 62-10567
Manufactured in the United States of America

The manuscript was received November 15, 1961, and published
February 27, 1962.

W. A. BENJAMIN, INC.

2465 Broadway
New York 25, New York

 # Prologue

Nearly sixty years ago, Emil Fischer described his experiments which led to the discovery of the structure of glucose and related sugars. In the past fifteen years Melvin Calvin and his associates have performed experiments leading to an understanding of the reactions used by photosynthetic organisms to make these sugars and many other compounds from carbon dioxide, water, and minerals, using the energy of light.

It was not long after the basic reaction of photosynthesis was recognized that speculation regarding its mechanism commenced. These discussions were carried forward first by Justus von Liebig and then by Adolf von Baeyer and, finally, by Richard Wilstatter and Arthur Stoll, into this century. However, it was the mechanism of the reverse pathway, that is, the combustion of carbohydrate to carbon dioxide and water with the utilization of the energy, which was first successfully mapped. This pathway was elucidated primarily by Otto Meyerhof and Hans Krebs.

Professor Calvin's interest in the basic process of solar energy conversion by green plants began about 1935, when he was studying with Professor Michael Polyani at Manchester. There he became interested in the remarkable properties of coordinated metal compounds, particularly metalloporphy-rins, as represented by heme and chlorophyll. He began a study on the electronic behavior of such compounds at that time. When Professor Calvin joined the Chemistry Depart-ment at Berkeley, these studies were encouraged by Professor Gilbert N. Lewis, and they have been continued to the present time. In time they will contribute to our understanding of the precise way in which chlorophyll and its relatives accomplish the primary quantum conversion into chemical potential, which is then used to drive the carbohydrate synthesis.

It has long been known that the reduction of carbon di-oxide to carbohydrate is probably a dark reaction, separate from the primary quantum conversion act. This knowledge stemmed from the early work of F. F. Blackman on the dark reactions of photosynthesis and its interpretation by Otto Warburg, and particularly from the comparative biochemical studies of Cornelius van Niel. Finally, Robert Hill separated the photo-induced production of molecular oxygen chemi-cally and physically from the reduction of carbon dioxide when he demonstrated oxygen evolution by illuminated chloroplasts, using ferric ion as an oxidant in place of carbon dioxide.

We can summarize the over-all conversion of light energy into chemical energy in the form of carbohydrate and oxygen by several steps. First, the light energy absorbed by chlorophyll and related pigments is converted into the high chemical potential energy of some compounds. Second, these compounds react with water and produce oxygen and good reducing agents as well as other cofactors containing high chemical potential energy. Finally, these reducing and ener-getic cofactors react with carbon dioxide and other inorganic compounds to produce organic compounds.

One of the principal difficulties in studying the synthetic pathway is that the machinery which converts carbon dioxide and minerals to organic compounds is itself composed of organic compounds made up of the same elements. Ordinary analytical methods do not allow us to distinguish easily between the machinery and its substrate. Fortunately, the discovery of the long-lived isotopic carbons (carbon-14) by Samual Rubin and Martin Kamen in 1940 provided the ideal tool for tracing these synthetic routes.

In 1945, carbon-14, radiocarbon, became available in large amounts as a product from nuclear reactors. With the encouragement and support of Professor Ernest O. Lawrence, the Director of the Radiation Laboratory in Berkeley, Professor Calvin began to study the pathway of carbon reduction during photosynthesis, using carbon-14 as his principal tool.

Among a number of people who were to be associated with him during the next few years of this work and who would all contribute to the success of the research, Dr. Andrew A. Benson was particularly instrumental, especially in the identification of the early products of photosynthetic carbon reduction. Key contributions to the development of the carbon reduction cycle were made by Dr. Peter Massini and Dr. Alex Wilson. Beginning as a graduate student with Professor Calvin in 1947, I have had the pleasure of being associated with him in this work to the present time.

The first big success came with Professor Calvin's identification of phosphoglyceric acid as the first stable product of carbon reduction during photosynthesis. Soon thereafter the application of two-dimensional paper chromatography combined with radioautography became an invaluable analytical tool for separating the minute amounts of radioactive ingredients formed in the plant. Identification of the remaining intermediates in the carbon reduction cycle soon followed, and these turned out to be all sugar phosphates.

A combination of kinetic studies on the appearance of carbon-14 in these intermediates, with degradation of the compounds that revealed the location of the radiocarbon in individual atoms, soon led to a linking together of a reaction sequence leading from phosphoglyceric acid through the several sugar phosphates. The experiments of Massini and Wilson helped to establish the carboxylation and reduction reactions of photosynthesis, and the cycle was complete.

In succeeding years much work has been done to check the validity of the cycle, to investigate details of its mechanism, and to establish its quantitative importance.

From almost the beginning of these studies we have been interested in reactions leading from the cycle to various other synthetic intermediates and end products, such as amino acids, sucrose and polysaccharides, and carboxylic acids. As a result of this work we have found that the photosynthetic machine, the chloroplast, is an even more complex and diversified apparatus than had been suspected. Not only does it manufacture sugars and other carbohydrates, but apparently nearly all other organic materials necessary for its continued growth as well.

In this book we review the evidence leading to the formulation of the carbon reduction cycle and discuss its quantitative importance. We describe as far as possible the biosynthetic pathways which we believe exist in the chloroplast. We show how newly reduced carbon from the carbon reduction cycle provides the starting material for these pathways. Our objective is to map complete synthetic sequences from carbon dioxide to final products. Three papers, of fundamental importance in the development of the theory regarding the path of carbon in photosynthesis, are included as reprints.

We are now just at the threshold of discovery of many of the biosynthetic pathways. There is good experimental evidence for some and a few clues for others, but for many we must speculate, relying on known, but nonphotosynthetic, pathways. We have called on our experience of some fifteen years' study of carbon fixation patterns during photosynthesis to provide us with clues. The clues help us to predict which reactions, which pathways, and which intermediates may be considered to be likely participants in the photosynthesis of carbon compounds.

This year Professor Calvin was awarded the Nobel Prize for his work on the assimilation of carbon dioxide during photosynthesis. Those who have worked with him and have experienced the stimulation provided by his enthusiasm and insight are especially delighted by this most well-deserved recognition of one of his many scientific achievements. Those of us who, under his leadership, have contributed something to the development of the carbon reduction cycle are particularly pleased to have been a part of this exciting work.

JAMES A. BASSHAM

Berkeley, California
December 1961

Acknowledgments

The publisher and the authors wish to acknowledge the assistance of the following organizations in the preparation of this volume:

The United States Atomic Energy Commission, which sponsored the preparation of this volume.

Verlag-Birkhäuser A.-G., Basel, for permission to reprint the article from *Experientia*.

The American Chemical Society, Washington, D.C., for permission to reprint the article from the *Journal of the American Chemical Society*.

Elsevier Publishing Co., Inc., Amsterdam, for permission to reprint the article from *Biochimica et Biophysica Acta*.

 Contents

Reprints

The photosynthesis
of carbon compounds

Introduction

Biosynthesis begins with photosynthesis. Green plants and other photosynthetic organisms use the energy of absorbed visible light to make organic compounds from inorganic compounds. These organic compounds are the starting point for all other biosynthetic pathways.

The products of photosynthesis provide not only the substrate material but also chemical energy for all subsequent biosynthesis. For example, nonphotosynthetic organisms making fats from sugars would first break down the sugars to smaller organic molecules. Some of the smaller molecules might be oxidized with O_2 to CO_2 and water. These reactions are accompanied by a release of chemical energy, because O_2 and sugar have a high chemical potential energy toward conversion to CO_2 and H_2O. In a biochemical system only part of this energy would be released as heat. The rest would be used to bring about the conversion of certain enzymic cofactors to their more energetic forms. These cofactors would then enter into specific enzymic reactions in such a way as to supply energy to drive reactions in the direction of fat synthesis. Fats would be formed from the small organic molecules resulting from the breakdown of sugars. Thus sugar, a photosynthetic product, can supply both the energy and the material for the biosynthesis of fats.

Photosynthetic organisms achieve energy storage through their ability to convert electromagnetic energy to chemical potential energy. The conversion begins when pigments absorb light energy. The absorbed energy changes the electronic configuration of the pigment molecule (chlorophyll) from its ground energy state to an excited state. The return of the pigment molecule to its ground-state energy level is accompanied by a (chemical) reaction that would not proceed without energy input; i.e., the products of this reaction have a smaller negative free energy of formation from their elements than do the reactants (in the same reaction). Thus some of the light energy is converted to chemical potential.

The detailed mechanism of all these energy-conversion steps is not known. However, the net result is often formulated by two chemical equations. One of these is an oxidation-reduction reaction resulting in the transfer of hydrogen from water to triphosphopyridine nucleotide (TPN):

$$(1) \quad HOH + TPN^+ \xrightarrow{\text{light}} \tfrac{1}{2}O_2 + TPNH + H^+$$

$$\Delta F' = +52.6 \text{ kcal*}$$

The other reaction is the formation of an anhydride, adenosine triphosphate (ATP), from the ions of two phosphoric acids, adenosine diphosphate and orthophosphate:

$$(2) \quad ADP^{3-} + HPO_4^= \xrightarrow{\text{light}} HOH + ATP^{4-} + H^+$$

$$\Delta F' = +11 \text{ kcal*}$$

In each of these reactions some of the light energy is stored as chemical potential, as indicated by the positive quantities for free energy change.

The structural formulas of these two cofactors are shown in Figure 1. TPNH and its close relative DPNH (reduced diphosphopyridine nucleotide) serve a double function in photosynthesis and in all biosynthesis. Both TPNH and

* Assuming these concentrations: $(TPNH) = (TPN^+)$, $(ATP^{4-}) = (ADP^{3-})$, $(H^+) = 10^{-7} M$, $(HPO_4^=) = 10^{-3} M$.

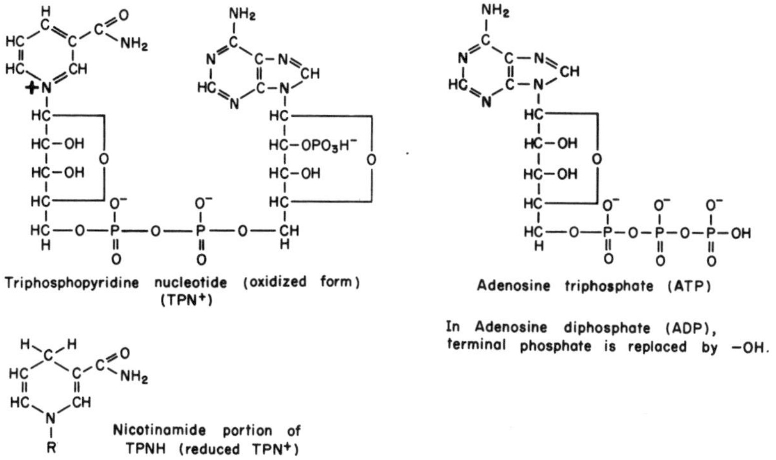

Figure 1. Formulas of TPN and ATP.

DPNH are reducing agents and carriers of chemical potential, in other words, strong reducing agents. Thus, one of their roles in biochemistry is analogous to that of H_2 in synthetic organic chemistry.

The function of ATP is to carry chemical potential and to act as a powerful phosphorylating agent. In the reduction of an acid to an aldehyde, important in photosynthesis, its role may be compared to that of a mineral acid anhydride in organic synthesis:

Organic synthesis:

5

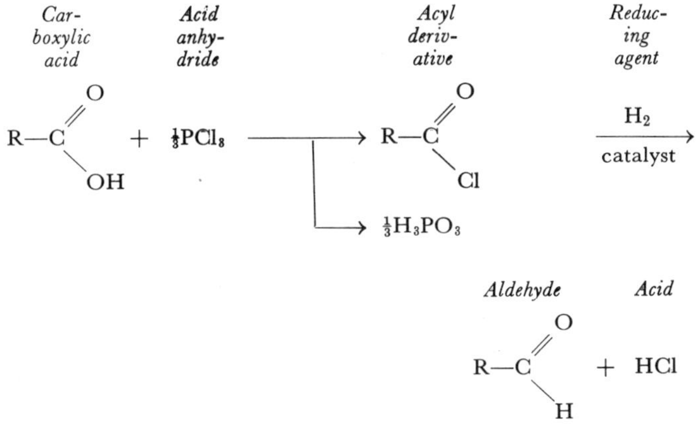

Biosynthesis:

| *Carboxylic* | *Acid* | | *Reducing* |
| *acid* | *anhydride* | *Acyl derivative* | *agent* |

$$(4) \quad R—C \underset{O^-}{\overset{O}{\diagup\diagdown}} + ADP—O—PO_3H \longrightarrow R—C \underset{OPO_3H^-}{\overset{O}{\diagup\diagdown}} \quad \underset{\text{enzyme}}{\overset{\text{TPNH}}{\longrightarrow}}$$

$$\longrightarrow ADP$$

| *Aldehyde* | *Acid* |

$$R—C \underset{O^-}{\overset{O}{\diagup\diagdown}} + HOPO_3H^-$$

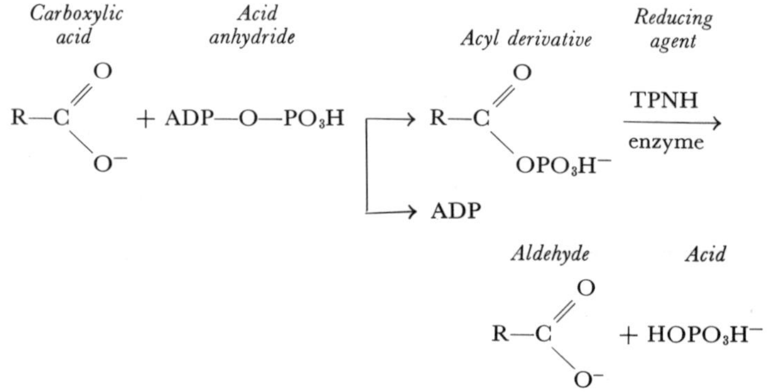

Among the many other reactions of ATP in biosynthesis, one, which is of considerable importance in photosynthesis, is the formation of sugar phosphates from sugars:

$$(5) \quad H^+ + ROH + ADP—O—PO_3H^- \rightarrow$$

$$R—OPO_3H^- + ADP + H_2O$$

The only known reactions of the carbon reduction cycle in photosynthesis which would require the use of TPNH and ATP are of the type shown in Eqs. (4) and (5). These reactions are the means by which chemical potential, derived from the absorbed light, is used to bring about the reduction and, transformation of carbon from CO_2 to organic compounds.

These two cofactors, ATP and TPNH, are at present the only ones that are known to be generated by the light reactions of photosynthesis and at the same time seem to be required for steps in the carbon reduction cycle. The possibility remains, however, that there are other energetic or reduced cofactors acting as carriers of hydrogen and energy from the light reactions to the carbon reduction cycle. Such unknown cofactors might substitute for or replace TPNH or ATP. They could, in fact, be more effective than the known cofactors, particularly *in vivo,* where they might well be built into the highly organized structure of the chloroplast. If such unknown cofactors do exist, they would have

6

to perform essentially the same functions as TPNH and ATP and would presumably be about as effective as carriers of chemical potential. In all discussions of the role of TPNH and ATP, the possibility of their replacement by as-yet-unidentified cofactors should be kept in mind.

For the purpose of discussion, let us consider the photosynthesis of carbon compounds as an isolated set of reactions. The principal substrates for this set of reactions are CO_2, hydrogen (as TPNH), phosphate (as ATP), and NH_4^+. The ammonium ion may be contained in the plant nutrient or it may be derived from the reduction of nitrate. If nitrate reduction is the source of NH_4^+, the energy for the reduction must also come from the light, at least indirectly. Other probable inorganic substrates for photosynthesis of organic compounds include sulfate, magnesium ion, and a number of trace elements. Many of these are required for growth in plants but may or may not be incorporated in organic compounds by photosynthesis.

Carbon
reduction cycle
of photosynthesis

We believe the principal pathways for the photosynthesis of simple organic compounds from CO_2 to be those shown in Figure 2 (1,2). The points at which ATP and TPNH act in these pathways are indicated. Kinetic studies (3) show that these pathways account for nearly all the carbon dioxide reduced during photosynthesis, at least in the unicellular algae *Chlorella pyrenoidosa*. From other investigations (4) it appears that the general metabolic sequence is the same in most respects for all photosynthetic organisms. (We shall discuss the recently proposed role of glycolic acid in CO_2 reduction in the section on Carboxylic Acids.)

The central feature of carbon-compound metabolism in photosynthesis is the carbon reduction cycle. Most of the carbon dioxide used is incorporated via this cycle. Pathways lead from intermediates in the cycle to various other important metabolites. A few of these pathways are shown in Figure 2.

The initial step for carbon dioxide incorporation in the cycle is the carboxylation of ribulose-1,5-diphosphate at the number 2 carbon atom of the sugar to give a highly labile β-keto acid. Evidence for the existence of this unstable intermediate has been adduced from *in vivo* studies (5). It has not been isolated in the *in vitro* reaction with the enzyme carboxydismutase. The product of the reaction *in vitro* is 2 molecules of 3-phosphoglyceric acid (PGA). The products in intact photosynthesizing cells may be 2 molecules of PGA or, as kinetic studies indicate (3), 1 molecule of PGA and 1 molecule of triose phosphate.

Once formed, the PGA is transformed in two ways. Some molecules are converted to products outside the cycle while the remainder are reduced to 3-phosphoglyceraldehyde via a reaction of the type shown in Eq. (4). The enzymes responsible for the two successive steps in the reduction are probably similar to phosphoglycerylkinase (6) and triose phosphate dehydrogenase (7–10).

The next phase of the carbon reduction cycle is the conversion of 5 molecules of triose phosphate to 3 molecules of pentose phosphate by a series of reactions. These reactions include condensations (aldolase), carbon-chain-length dismutations (transketolase), removal of phosphate groups (phosphatase), and interconversions of different pentose phosphates (isomerase, epimerase). Enzyme systems that catalyze reactions similar to these steps are listed in Table 2. The sequence of steps may be seen in the cycle diagram (Figure 2).

The various pentose phosphates are converted to ribulose-5-phosphate. The final step is the formation of ribulose diphosphate (RuDP) from ribulose-5-phosphate. This step requires 1 molecule of ATP [Eq. (5)].

For every reaction in the cycle to occur at least once (a complete turn of the cycle), the carboxylation reaction must occur three times. The net result of each *complete* turn of the cycle is the incorporation of 3 molecules of CO_2 and the production of 1 three-carbon (or ½ six-carbon) organic molecule. Each complete turn of the cycle would require 6 molecules of TPNH or equivalent reducing cofactor (2 per CO_2) and 9 molecules of ATP, if each C_6 carboxylation product is split to 2 molecules of PGA and if all the PGA

9

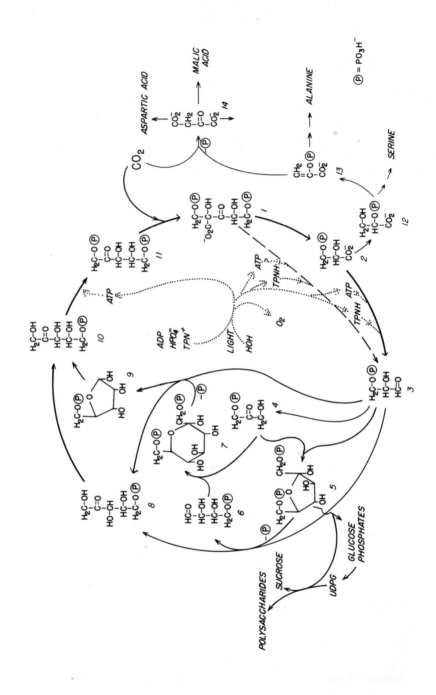

is reduced to triose phosphate. If the carboxylation product is reductively split (dashed line in Figure 2) the requirement for TPNH would probably be the same, that is, 6 molecules per complete turn of the cycle. In this case, however, the cycle might require either 9 molecules of ATP or only 6.

Figure 2. Carbon reduction pathways in photosynthesis. Compounds: (1) 2-carboxy-3-keto-1,5-diphosphoribitol, (2) 3-phosphoglyceric acid (3-PGA), (3) glyceraldehyde-3-phosphate, (4) dihydroxyacetone phosphate, (5) fructose-1,6-diphosphate, (6) erythrose-4-phosphate, (7) sedoheptulose-1,7-diphosphate, (8) xylulose-5-phosphate, (9) ribose-5-phosphate, (10) ribulose-5-phosphate, (11) ribulose-1,5-diphosphate, (12) 2-phosphoglyceric acid (2-PGA), (13) phosphoenolpyruvic acid (PEPA), (14) oxalacetic acid. −ⓟ: fructose diphosphate and sedoheptulose diphosphate lose one phosphate group before transketolase reaction occurs.

Evidence
for the carbon
reduction cycle

The carbon reduction cycle in essentially the form shown in Figure 2 was mapped during the period between 1946 and 1953 (11–17). The experiments, results, and interpretations leading to its formulation have been extensively discussed elsewhere (2). They will be briefly reviewed here, not necessarily in chronological order.

The carbon that enters the plants' metabolism has been followed through the various intermediate compounds by labeling the carbon dioxide with radiocarbon, C^{14}. The analysis of the labeled compounds has been carried out by paper chromatography and radioautography. The interpretation of results leading to the cycle formulation has been based on the kinetics of the appearance of C^{14} in various identified compounds as a function of time of photosynthesis with $C^{14}O_2$ and other variables.

The methods are best described by an illustration. Consider a simple experiment with a suspension of the algae *Chlorella pyrenoidosa*, very extensively used in these studies. These green unicellular plants, suspended in water containing the necessary inorganic ions (nitrate, phosphate, etc.) and aerated with a stream of $C^{12}O_2$ (ordinary carbon dioxide),

12

photosynthesize at a rapid rate if illuminated from each side in a thin transparent vessel. The CO_2 is continually taken up from the solution (where it is in equilibrium with bicarbonate ion) and converted by the photosynthetic plant through a series of biochemical intermediates to various organic products.

A solution of radioactive bicarbonate, $HC^{14}O_3^-$, is suddenly introduced into the algae suspension. The plant does not distinguish in any important way between the C^{12} and C^{14}, which are chemically almost identical. Immediately some of the C^{14} is incorporated into the first of the biochemical intermediate compounds. As time passes the C^{14} gets into subsequent intermediates in the chain. After a few seconds exposure to the $C^{14}O_2$, the suspension of algae is run into methanol to a final concentration of 80 per cent methanol. This treatment denatures all the enzyme instantly and freezes the pattern of C^{14} labeling by preventing further change. Now the dead plant material is analyzed for radioactive compounds to see which are the first stable products of carbon reduction during photosynthesis.

The first step in this analysis is to prepare an extract of the soluble compounds. The early products of carbon reduction have been found to be simple soluble molecules. This extract is then concentrated and analyzed by the method of two-dimensional paper chromatography (12). The importance of the method for these studies stems from the fact that it permits the analysis of a few micrograms or less of dozens of different substances in a single simple operation.

Of these many compounds, those into which the plant incorporates C^{14} during its few seconds of photosynthesis with $HC^{14}O_3^-$ are radioactive and omit the particles resulting from radioactive decay of the C^{14}. In this case these are β particles, and these may be detected by the fact that they expose x-ray film. Thus, if a sheet of x-ray film is placed in contact with the two-dimensional paper chromatogram, subsequent development of the film will show a black spot on the film corresponding to the exact shape and location of

13

each radioactive compound on the paper. A quantitative determination of the amount of radiocarbon in each compound may then be made by placing a Geiger-Müller tube with a very thin window over the radioactive compound on the paper and counting electronically the emitted β particles.

The next stage in the method of radiochromatographic analysis is the identification of the radioactive compounds. This identification is accomplished in a variety of ways. When a familiar set of chromatographic solvents has been used, the position of an unknown compound compared to the positions of known substances provides a clue to its identity. The next step may be elution or washing of the compound off the paper and the determination of such chemical and physical properties (e.g., the distribution coefficient) of the substance as can be measured with a solution of a few micrograms or less of the material. These properties are then compared with those of known compounds. The final check on the identity of the compound is frequently made by placing on the same spot on filter paper the radioactive compound and 10 to 100 μg of the pure nonradioactive substance with which the radioactive compound is thought to be identical. The new chromatogram is then developed. A radioautograph is prepared to locate the radioactive substance, after which the paper is sprayed with a chemical spray (for example, ninhydrin for amino acids), which produces a color where the carrier compound is located on the paper. Superposition of the paper chromatogram and the radioautograph (x-ray film) will show an exact coincidence between chemically developed color on the paper and the black spot on the film, provided the two substances are identical.

Once the identity of the radioactive compounds formed during a short period of photosynthesis had been established, experiments were performed under a variety of conditions and times of exposure of the algae to radiocarbon.

The radioautogram from the experiment with Chlorella described above is shown in Figure 3. Even after only 10 seconds of exposure to C^{14}, a dozen or more compounds are found. Some of these (the sugar phosphates) are not separated from each other by the first chromatography and must be subjected to further analysis. When the sugar monophosphates are hydrolyzed to remove the phosphate groups and rechromatographed, separate spots are found of triose (dihydroxyacetone), tetrose, pentoses (ribulose, xylulose, and ribose), hexoses (glucose and fructose), and heptose (sedoheptulose). The radioactive sugar diphosphates area gives free ribulose, fructose, glucose, and sedoheptulose.

After periods of photosynthesis with C^{14} of less than 5 seconds, 3-phosphoglyceric acid (PGA) was found to be the predominant radioactive product. Chemical degradation of this compound showed that the radioactivity first appears in the carboxyl carbon (14). Later kinetic studies showed that the rate of incorporation of C^{14} into PGA at very short times was much greater than the rate of labeling of any other compound (18,1). Therefore, it was concluded that PGA is the first stable product of carbon dioxide fixation during photosynthesis, and, furthermore, that carbon dioxide first enters the carboxyl group of PGA, presumably via a carboxylation reaction.

Further reactions in the photosynthetic sequence were

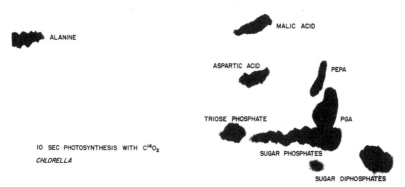

Figure 3. Radioautograph of two-dimensional paper chromatogram. Alcoholic extract of *Chlorella pyrenoidosa* after 10 seconds photosynthesis with $C^{14}O_2$.

15

suggested by the already known pathways of the glycolytic breakdown of sugars, which lead to PGA as an intermediate. Since the sugar phosphates are important early products of carbon reduction in photosynthesis, it was proposed that they are formed from PGA by a reversal of the glycolytic pathway. Degradation of the radioactive hexoses from short experiments showed that they were labeled in the two center carbon atoms (numbers 3 and 4) just as one would expect if 2 molecules of carboxyl-labeled PGA were first reduced to triose and then linked together by the two labeled carbon atoms to give hexose (Figure 4).

The hexose and triose phosphates may be converted by aldolase or transaldolase and transketolase enzymes to pentose and heptose phosphates (Figure 2 and Table 2). Degradation of these sugars and comparison of the labeling patterns within the molecules showed that this conversion did occur, and in such a way that 5 molecules of triose phos-

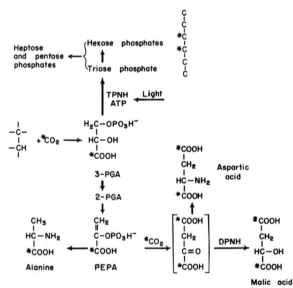

Figure 4. Labeling of compounds with C^{14} during early steps in carbon dioxide reduction during photosynthesis with $C^{14}O_2$.

16

phate were ultimately converted to 3 molecules of pentose phosphate.

Other known metabolic pathways leading from PGA (Figure 4) give rise first to phosphoenolpyruvic acid (PEPA), which then may undergo further transformations, including the following: (1) it may be carboxylated and transaminated to give aspartic acid, (2) it may be carboxylated and reduced to give malic acid, or (3) it may be dephosphorylated and transaminated to give alanine. All these compounds are labeled after short exposures of the algae to $HC^{14}O_3^-$ in the light.

The enzyme system of plants, which during respiration brings about the oxidation of triose phosphate to PGA in the glycolytic pathway, was known to produce ATP and TPNH (or DPNH). If PGA is to be reduced to triose phosphate during photosynthesis, it follows that ATP and TPNH must be supplied. We have already seen that these two cofactors, and possibly others, are produced as a consequence of the light reaction and the splitting of water. It might be expected that, if the light were turned off from plants photosynthesizing in ordinary carbon dioxide at precisely the same time that $C^{14}O_2$ is introduced, PGA would no longer be reduced to sugar phosphates but would still be formed (if no light-produced cofactors are required for the carboxylation reaction). Moreover, the PGA would still be used in other reactions not requiring these cofactors. In Figure 5, the radioautograph from just such an experiment, this prediction proves to be correct. Labeled PGA is still formed by the algae from $C^{14}O_2$ during 20 seconds in the dark, but only a very little of the PGA is reduced to sugar phosphates. At the same time, a large amount of alanine is formed from PGA via PEPA in reactions that do not require ATP. The trace of labeled sugar phosphates that does appear may be due to the residual ATP, or some unknown cofactor, which was formed while the light was on but which had not yet been used up when the $C^{14}O_2$ was introduced. The formation of malic acid and of alanine and aspartic acid

17

in the dark indicates the presence of some reducing cofactors, either remaining from the light or derived from some other metabolic reaction.

Before we discuss the evidence for the remainder of the carbon reduction cycle, we must describe another type of experiment with $C^{14}O_2$ and photosynthesizing algae. In these experiments, algae are first permitted to photosynthesize for 20 minutes or more in the presence of a constant supply of $C^{14}O_2$. During this time environmental conditions are maintained nearly constant (temperature, CO_2 pressure, light intensity, etc.). After about 10 minutes of exposure to $C^{14}O_2$, so much radiocarbon has passed through the various biochemical intermediate compounds on its way to end products that each carbon atom of each intermediate compound contains, on the average, the same percentage of C^{14} atoms as the CO_2 being absorbed. In other words, the specific radioactivities of all the carbon atoms of all the early intermediates are the same as the specific radioactivity of the entering radiocarbon, which can be measured.

At this point samples of the algae are removed without disturbing the rest of the algae, and these samples are killed and subsequently analyzed by the methods described. The

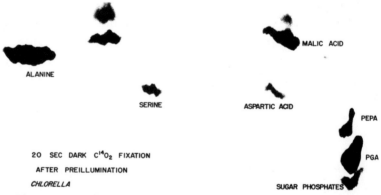

Figure 5. Radioautograph of chromatogram of products of 20 seconds $C^{14}O_2$ fixation by *Chlorella pyrenoidosa* in the dark following a period of photosynthesis.

total radioactivity of each intermediate is measured, and, when this is divided by the known *specific radioactivity* of the entering CO_2, the total number of carbon atoms of each intermediate compound in the sample can be calculated. Thus the number of moles per unit volume of algae of the various intermediates of the actively photosynthesizing system may be determined. This number of moles per unit volume of plant material is an average concentration, since the distribution of molecules in such a heterogeneous system is not homogeneous.

This determination of the concentrations of intermediates *in vivo* is an extremely valuable tool which has many uses, but let us proceed for the moment with one particular application. Having taken a sample of algae for later determination of the concentrations of compounds, the experimenter turns off the light and proceeds to take a series of samples of the algae as rapidly as possible, which is about every 3 seconds. When the concentrations of compounds in these samples are determined, any changes resulting from turning off the light will be revealed. The two most striking changes are found to be in the concentration of PGA, which increases rapidly, and in the concentration of one particular compound, ribulose diphosphate, which drops rapidly to zero (16,20).

The increase in PGA on turning off the light is expected. The cofactors, derived from the light reaction, are necessary for the reduction of PGA. The rapid drop in ribulose diphosphate, taken together with the fact that other sugar phosphates initially do not drop rapidly in concentration, indicates that the formation of ribulose diphosphate from other sugar phosphates requires a light-formed cofactor. This conclusion agrees with the fact that the known enzyme, which converts ribulose-5-phosphate to ribulose-1,5-diphosphate (RuDP), requires ATP (Table 2). The drop in ribulose diphosphate, alone among the sugar phosphates, means that it is being used up by a reaction that does not require light.

Ribulose diphosphate, then, is used up by some reaction

that proceeds in the dark, and PGA continues to be formed in the dark. Could the carboxylation of ribulose diphosphate to form PGA be the first step in carbon dioxide reduction? To answer this question, an experiment similar to the one just described was performed. This time, however, instead of turning off the light, the light was left on, and carbon dioxide was suddenly removed (19). The result of this experiment was that the concentration of ribulose diphosphate now rose rapidly while PGA dropped rapidly. Thus the carboxylation of RuDP to give PGA was confirmed.

The
 carboxylation
reactions

Thus far we have mentioned two carboxylation reactions in photosynthesis: carboxylation of RuDP (the carbon reduction cycle) and carboxylation of PEPA. When algae have been allowed to photosynthesize for less than a minute, virtually all the radioactivity found on the chromatogram prepared from the algae is located in compounds apparently derived from these two reactions. There still remained the possibility that other carboxylation reactions might occur which would involve intermediate compounds too unstable or too volatile to be seen on the chromatograms. These possibilities were tested by making a quantitative comparison between the rate of uptake of $C^{14}O_2$ from the medium and the rate of appearance of C^{14} in compounds on the chromatograms (3).

For these experiments, the algae were kept, as close as possible, in steady-state growth in the experimental vessel. Light, temperature, pH, and supply of inorganic nutrients were kept constant. Gas was circulated through the algae suspension in a closed system by means of a pump. Levels of CO_2, O_2, and, when present, $C^{14}O_2$, were continuously measured and recorded. From the known gas volumes of the

21

system and the recorded rates of changes in gas tensions, we calculated the total change in these gases as a function of time. Then we added $C^{14}O_2$ to the system and took samples of algae every few seconds for the first few minutes and then less frequently up to an hour. Each sample of algae was killed immediately and a portion analyzed as described earlier. A part of each sample was reserved and was dried on a planchet to determine the rate of appearance of C^{14} in all stable nonvolatile compounds. This rate proved to be the same as the externally measured rate of uptake of CO_2 and C^{14} between 20 and 60 seconds after the addition of C^{14}. If unstable or volatile intermediates do precede these stable compounds, they are equivalent in micromoles of carbon to no more than 5 seconds photosynthetic fixation, according to the shape of the fixation curve during the first 20 seconds.

We analyzed each sample by paper chromatography and determined the radioactivity in each compound in each sample. On the basis of the externally measured uptake rates, at least 85 per cent of the carbon was found to be incorporated into individual compounds on the paper chromatograms during the first 40 seconds. At least 70 per cent of the total carbon uptake rate could be accounted for by the appearance of C^{14} in compounds apparently derived from the RuDP carboxylation reaction of the carbon reduction cycle via the pathways shown in Figure 2. Another 5 per cent or more was found to be incorporated via C_1-C_3 carboxylation. About 5 per cent was found in unidentified compounds or in glutamic acid, whose photosynthetic pathway is not definitely known. Of the 15 per cent not accounted for, some may be in nonextractable polysaccharides, whose sugar phosphate precursors become labeled very quickly. More of the unaccounted-for radiocarbon is undoubtedly in a large number of unmeasured compounds on the chromatograms. Each of these compounds contains by itself too little C^{14} to be readily determined. In any event, it is clear that the known fixation pathways are the only quantitatively important ones unless there are unknown pathways utilizing the same intermediate compounds.

A kinetic analysis of the appearance of C^{14} in PGA and RuDP in this experiment indicated that the carboxylation reaction results in the formation of only *one* free molecule of PGA per molecule of CO_2 entering the cycle. The kinetic analysis cannot say what the other three-carbon fragment would be. It might be merely a molecule of PGA bound in some way so that its labeling remains distinct from that of the PGA from the other half of the six-carbon addition product. The only other compounds that seem to satisfy the kinetic requirements and that could readily result from the splitting of the six-carbon addition product are the triose phosphates. The formation of a molecule of triose phosphate in this way would require a reductive split of the addition product, as indicated by the dashed line in Figure 2.

That such a pathway differing from the *in vitro* reaction may exist seems entirely reasonable, since the enzymes of the carbon reduction cycle appear to be closely associated with the molecular structures in which the TPNH is formed in the chloroplast (21). In the intact plant the carboxylation enzyme, as well as the enzyme responsible for the splitting of the product and the enzyme that brings about the reduction of TPN^+ to TPNH, might be part of a structurally organized system. In fact, if a reductive scission does occur, the reducing agent could be a substance formed from the oxidation of water and preceding TPNH in the electron transport chain. This substance might never be available in sufficient concentration to be a factor in *in vitro* systems in which carboxydismutase is coupled with isolated or broken chloroplasts. Such an explanation of the experimentally observed kinetic result is purely hypothetical. *We mention it to focus attention on the possibility that a given biosynthetic pathway may follow a different course in an intact cell than that which would be predicted on the basis of studies with fragmented cells or enzymes alone.*

23

In higher plants much of the product of photosynthesis must be transported to a nonphotosynthetic part of the plant. This requires that higher proportions of easily transported molecules such as sucrose are formed (4). In all higher plants that have been studied, however, there is appreciable direct photosynthesis of amino acids and fats, not just carbohydrates.

Balance among synthetic pathways

We have seen that in each complete turn of the carbon-reduction cycle 3 molecules of RuDP (15 carbon atoms) are carboxylated by 3 molecules of CO_2 to give 6 three-carbon compounds (18 carbon atoms). Thus there is a net gain of 3 reduced carbon atoms. These atoms are withdrawn from the cycle for further synthesis. They may be withdrawn from the cycle as PGA or as any of the sugar phosphates in the cycle. Before the photosynthetic reactions had been mapped, it was commonly believed that photosynthesis leads first to carbohydrates only and that these carbohydrates are then converted via nonphotosynthetic reactions to other compounds such as amino acids and fatty acids. We now know that pathways leading from the carbon reduction cycle to amino acids and fatty acids and other substances can be just as important quantitatively as those leading to carbohydrates. This is particularly true in a unicellular algae, as exemplified by *Chlorella pyrenoidosa*, where under some conditions less than half of the assimilated carbon is directly converted into carbohydrate. This carbohydrate synthesis draws its carbon from the cycle in the form of sugar phosphates. Consequently, more than half of the carbon drained from the carbon reduction cycle as PGA or sugar phosphates may be used in fat and protein synthesis.

It is interesting to consider an extreme case in which all the carbon assimilated by the carbon reduction cycle would be withdrawn from the cycle as PGA, converted to PEPA, and then carboxylated to give four-carbon compounds. In this case, 75 per cent of the assimilated carbon would enter the photosynthetic pathways via the carbon reduction cycle, while the remaining 25 per cent would enter via the carboxylation of PEPA.

With normal conditions of steady-state growth under high light intensity, the ratios of various fixation pathways must be determined to a large extent by the requirements of the plant for the small molecules from which the protein, carbohydrate, fat, and other substances of the plant are synthesized.

Photosynthesis vs. other forms of biosynthesis

Biosyntheic reactions in plants cannot be classified as photosynthetic or nonphotosynthetic on the basis of direct photochemical action because all reactions in the synthetic pathways are probably "dark" reactions. However, we can make a classification on the basis of the immediate source of the required cofactors. The conversion of light energy results in the formation of ATP and TPNH and perhaps other unknown cofactors. When these cofactors are formed by the light reaction and are used to bring about the synthesis of carbon compounds, we may consider the reactions to be photosynthetic. Also included in this category would be preliminary and intermediate steps such as hydrations, condensations, and carboxylations.

It may well be that all photosynthetic reactions, as just defined, occur in the chloroplasts while the light is on. If this is true, reactions outside the chloroplast would derive their energy from substrate carbon compounds which diffuse from the chloroplast to the extrachloroplastic spaces of the cell. Such an interpretation is suggested by the report by Tolbert (22), who found that chloroplasts isolated from Swiss chard, when allowed to photosynthesize with $HC^{14}O_3^-$, excreted mainly glycolic acid into the medium. Phosphate esters, of importance to the carbon reduction cycle, were retained in the chloroplasts. Isolated chloroplasts have a carbon metabolism that is much more limited than photosynthesis in intact cells. This is probably due to loss of enzymic activity by chloroplasts during the isolation process. In all probability the carbon compounds excreted by intact chloroplasts *in vivo* include substances other than glycolate.

There is more than a semantic reason for making a distinction between photosynthetic and nonphotosynthetic pathways. The environment of the photosynthetic metabolism is unique. There is an abundance of the reduced and energetic form of the coenzymes. Hence synthetic pathways do not require energy derived from degradative reactions such as decarboxylations and oxidations. For example, a well-known biosynthetic pathway leading to glutamic acid from acetate includes oxidative and decarboxylation steps. Such a pathway is to be expected in a nonphotosynthetic system, where degradation of part of the substrate is the only means of obtaining the energy and reducing power for synthetic reactions. In a photosynthetic system one might expect instead a pathway involving only condensations, reductions, and carboxylations. We cannot say that this difference in type of reaction will always be borne out by the actual mechanisms when they are known. This proposed difference in reaction type may be a useful working hypothesis to those who attempt to map photosynthetic pathways from experimental data.

Amino acid synthesis

Among the first compounds found to be labeled by photosynthesis of $C^{14}O_2$ in algae were alanine, aspartic acid, and several other amino acids (11). These compounds were slowly labeled even in the dark when algae were exposed to $C^{14}O_2$. They and malic acid were much more rapidly labeled if the algae were photosynthesizing, or had been photosynthesizing, just prior to the moment of addition of $C^{14}O_2$. We recognized that these amino acids were therefore products of photosynthetic reduction of CO_2, even though they could also become labeled by reversible respiratory reactions. Accelerated incorporation of C^{14} into amino acids in higher plants during photosynthesis has been noted in this laboratory (23,24) and in many others (25–28). Nichiporovich (25) has presented and reviewed evidence that synthesis of proteins in the chloroplasts of higher plants is greatly accelerated during photosynthesis. This accelerated protein synthesis appears to occur directly from the intermediates of photosynthetic carbon reduction, since the proteins were labeled when $C^{14}O_2$ was used but not when C^{14}-labeled carbohydrate was administered. Photosynthetically accelerated synthesis of protein containing N^{15} was also observed when $N^{15}H_4^+$ was administered. Sissakian (29) has reviewed evidence that protein can be synthesized in isolated chloroplasts from nonprotein nitrogen, including peptides.

In experiments in this laboratory (30) it recently has been possible to measure the proportion of the total carbon fixed by *Chlorella pyrenoidosa,* which is directly incorporated into certain key amino acids. These experiments show that, during steady-state photosynthesis in bright light with an adequate supply of inorganic nutrients, the synthesis of these amino acids can account for 60 per cent of all the carbon fixed by the algae and 30 per cent of the uptake of NH_4^+, which is also measured. If the light is turned off, the NH_4^+ uptake and C^{14} fixation into amino acids are both accelerated for about 10 minutes and then drop to a very small fraction of the rates in the light. Finally, these experiments indicate clearly that in *Chlorella pyrenoidosa* there are at least two pools of alanine, glutamic acid, aspartic acid, and serine, and probably other amino acids as well. One of these pools, especially in the cases of alanine and aspartic acid, is labeled extremely rapidly after the introduction of $C^{14}O_2$ to the algae. So rapidly are these compounds labeled, in fact, that the site of their synthesis must be freely accessible to their photosynthetically formed precursors, namely, phosphoenol-pyruvic acid and PGA (see Figure 1). The studies of Tolbert (22) and Moses et al. (31) indicate that the photosynthetic pools are isolated from the extrachloroplastic region. We conclude, therefore, that in Chlorella the more rapidly labeled pools of amino acids are located at the site of photosynthetic carbon reduction, probably in the chloroplast.

The rates of flow of carbon through these pools of amino acids as determined from kinetic labeling data with Chlorella in a typical experiment are shown in Table 1.

The amino acids shown in Table 1 are those most prominently labeled with C^{14} during a few minutes of photosynthesis. In addition, a number of other amino acids become labeled as time passes. The rates of labeling seem to indicate that the carbon skeletons of these other acids are probably

Table 1

Rates of Flow of Carbon through Active Pools of Amino Acids

Compound	Calculated rate of synthesis R, μmoles of carbon	Equiv. NH_4^+ uptake, μmoles of NH_4^+
Alanine	2.67	0.89
Serine	0.49	0.16
Aspartic acid	0.89	0.22
Glutamic acid	0.98	0.20
Glutamine	0.32	0.13
Glycine[a]	0.04	0.02
Citrulline[b]	0.09	0.09
Threonine[a]	0.20	0.05
Total	5.44	1.69
Externally measured uptake	17.0	2.6
% of total through these pools	32	65

[a] Not included in totals.

[b] Figures are for carbamyl carbon only.

derived, for the most part, from the listed amino acids. However, the aromatic rings of the amino acids are synthesized by another pathway.

In Table 1 we compare the rates of synthesis of carbon skeletons that have been measured with the rate of uptake of NH_4^+. The rate of synthesis of any given amino acid does not necessarily represent the rate of incorporation of inorganic nitrogen into that amino acid, since it could be formed by transamination from another amino acid. However, the total of the rates of synthesis of all "primary" amino acids should account for the major fraction of the rate of uptake of ammonia. By "primary" amino acids we mean those amino acids whose carbon skeletons are not synthesized from some other amino acid. Alanine, serine, and aspartic acid are clearly primary amino acids, since their rates of labeling reach a maximum as soon as the intermediates in the carbon reduction cycle are saturated (about 3 minutes in this experiment) and long before they themselves, or any other amino acids, are saturated with radiocarbon (30). Probably glutamic acid is a primary amino acid also, but kinetic data alone cannot prove this at the moment. Glutamine is generally supposed to arise from glutamic acid, but there is some evidence to indicate that it may arise as a primary amino acid amide (32,30).

In any event, the rates of synthesis of alanine, serine, and aspartic acid in reservoirs we believe to be closely associated with the chloroplasts in Chlorella are great enough to permit the following conclusions.

1. An appreciable fraction of the carbon assimilated during photosynthesis in Chlorella is used directly in the synthesis of amino acids without the intermediacy of sugars or any other class of compounds except acid phosphates and carboxylic acids.

2. Since this amino acid synthesis accounts for a major portion of the inorganic nitrogen uptake, these amino acids must be used to a large extent in protein synthesis. However, some important amino acids (i.e., glycine) are so slowly labeled that they probably do not supply a major part of the carbon for protein synthesis. Instead, the carbon skeletons corresponding to these amino acids must be incorporated into protein in some form other than as the free amino acid.

Before considering synthetic routes to specific amino acids, we wish to reiterate our belief that photosynthetic reactions need not follow the same course as the better-known synthetic reactions of other nonphotosynthetic organisms. Also note that few if any enzymes involved in amino acid synthesis have ever been isolated from chloroplasts. Thus we are forced to suggest new and untested hypothetical paths. Our guiding principles will be that chemical potential should be used to drive the reactions rapidly in the forward direction and that loss of carbon or reduction level should be avoided wherever possible.

In Figure 6 are shown hypothetical pathways leading from PGA to alanine, serine, aspartic acid, and malic acid. These pathways differ somewhat from known enzymatic pathways, in that, in each step leading to the amino acid, ammonia reacts with a phosphoric acid ester.

The rapid incorporation of inorganic nitrogen into organic compounds would be brought about by the large negative free-energy change associated with each of these reactions. Thus these reactions, and not the reductive amination of ketoglutaric acid alone, would account for a major portion of ammonia incorporation during photosynthesis.

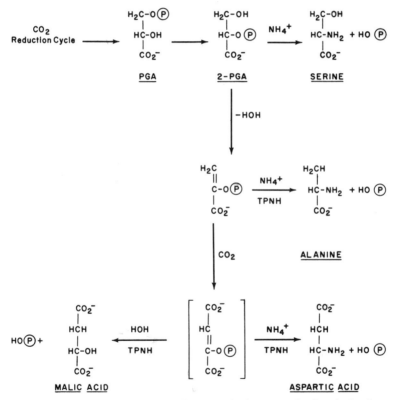

Figure 6. Hypothetical pathways of photosynthesis of alanine, aspartic acid, serine, and malic acid.

This seems entirely reasonable when one considers that PGA is both the immediate precursor in these reactions and the primary product of carbon reduction during photosynthesis. These amino acids could then supply ammonia via transaminase reactions for the synthesis of many other amino acids. Holm-Hansen et al. (33) have demonstrated the presence of a transaminase activity in spinach chloroplasts, which is very effective in the transfer of amino groups from unlabeled alanine to C^{14}-labeled pyruvic acid.

The three-carbon precursors to these amino acids are in rapid equilibrium with PGA. PEPA becomes C^{14}-saturated during photosynthesis in $C^{14}O_2$ in Chlorella almost as soon as PGA itself. The proposed phosphoenoloxalacetate probably does not exist except in enzyme complexes. Thus, by the time the PGA is C^{14}-saturated, these amino acids are being labeled as rapidly as if they were formed directly from $C^{14}O_2$.

It has been suggested that glutamic acid is formed during photosynthesis by a carboxylation of γ-aminobutyric acid (34). Judging by our studies with *Chlorella pyrenoidosa* during steady-state photosynthesis with $C^{14}O_2$, this reaction apparently does not constitute a source of glutamate, since γ-aminobutyric acid does not become labeled, even by the time the glutamic acid is 50 per cent saturated with C^{14} and long after the rate of labeling of glutamic acid has passed its maximum. Clearly, a compound cannot be a precursor in a steady-state system unless it is itself continuously regenerated. If the reaction does occur at all, the glutamic acid so formed could only be a shuttle for CO_2, regenerating unlabeled γ-aminobutyric acid. Even so, such a carboxylation reaction does not account for more than about 1 per cent of the carbon fixed in our studies of steady-state CO_2 fixation by Chlorella.

One possible route from PGA to glutamic acid would begin with conversion of PGA to PEPA, followed by carboxylation of PEPA to give oxalacetic acid. Condensation of oxalacetic acid with acetyl CoA would give citric acid, thence aconitic acid, thence isocitric acid. Proceeding along the Kreb's cycle, the next two steps are *oxidation* to oxalo-succinic acid, followed by *oxidation and decarboxylation* to give α-ketoglutaric acid. Finally, the reductive amination would give glutamic acid. This pathway may be followed in *Chlorella pyrenoidosa* in the synthesis of glutamic acid, par-ticularly when the light is turned off. We suspect that it is not the principal pathway during photosynthesis for two rea-sons, one experimental and one theoretical. Experimentally, the rates of labeling of the intermediate compounds such as citric acid and ketoglutaric acid are too slow to permit them to serve as precursors to the more rapidly labeled reservoir of glutamic acid. Theoretically, the pathway is objectionable to us as a photosynthetic route because it involves two oxida-tions and a decarboxylation.

How else might glutamic acid be formed during photo-synthesis? The availability of three-carbon and two-carbon compounds suggests the possibility of a simple condensation. Barker and co-workers (35–37) found an enzymic pathway in certain microorganisms leading from glutamic acid to py-ruvic acid and acetate via citramalate, mesaconic acid, and β-methylaspartate. The reverse of this pathway might operate during photosynthesis also. However, we have been unable so far to find significant amounts of radiocarbon in either β-methylaspartic acid or mesaconic acid in Chlorella which were synthesizing glutamic acid from $C^{14}O_2$. Moreover, a gen-eral energy-conserving principle would suggest that PEPA and not free pyruvic acid should be the three-carbon com-pound that combines with the two-carbon fragment. As we shall see in the discussion for the synthesis of aromatic rings, it has been proposed that PEPA can condense with an alde-hyde, erythrose phosphate, to give (eventually) phosphoshi-kimic acid (38). Perhaps a similar reaction between PEPA and glyoxylic acid could lead to a product such as γ-hydroxy-glutamic acid, which could be subsequently converted to glutamic acid. Dekker (39) has reported the presence of an enzyme in rat liver that converts γ-hydroxyglutamic acid to glyoxylate and another product, which may be alanine. The presence of γ-hydroxyglutamic acid in green leaves has been reported by Virtanen and Hietala (40). The dehydration and reduction of γ-hydroxyglutamic acid to give glutamic acid would be common types of biochemical reactions, analogous to the formation of succinic acid from malic acid. However, we have at present no experimental evidence for such a pathway.

Threonine does not become labeled as rapidly as the amino acids so far discussed, and it may well be secondary in origin. That is, it may be an example of conversion of primary amino acids (aspartic acid, alanine, serine, and glutamic acid) to other amino acids of their respective families, a process that presumably occurs in photosynthesis.

The small amount of labeled glycine formed during steady-state photosynthesis may come from either serine or glyoxylic acid.

Carboxylic acids

Malic and fumaric acids

Malic acid and fumaric acid are rapidly labeled during steady-state photosynthesis with $C^{14}O_2$. These acids are probably formed by reduction of the product of carboxylation of PEPA. In the steady-state experiment that yielded the results shown in Table 1, about 5 per cent of the C^{14} uptake rate could be accounted for in the labeling of these two acids. In that experiment very little of the radioactivity finds its way into succinic acid. It would thus appear that, if malic and fumaric acids are labeled by reductive carboxylation of PEPA, either (1) the reaction sequence is highly reversible, leading to exchange labeling, or (2) the malic and succinic acids are converted to other compounds by as-yet-undetermined paths.

The probability of labeling via exchange (1) may be answered by a thermodynamic argument. Under the conditions existing in the chloroplast during photosynthesis, the actual free energy change accompanying the conversion of PEPA, CO_2, TPNH, and either ADP or IDP to malic acid,

TPN$^+$, and ATP or ITP is probably at least -7 kcal. The ratio of the forward reaction to the back reaction, given by

$$\Delta F = -RT \ln \left(\frac{\text{forward rate}}{\text{back rate}} \right)$$

$$= -RT \ln \left(\frac{\text{back rate plus net rate}}{\text{back rate}} \right)$$

would thus be 10^5 or greater. Since the rate of labeling of malic acid is measurable and gives the net rate by a simple calculation, the back reaction, and hence the exchange labeling, can be shown to be of negligible importance.

This type of calculation is of considerable importance in *in vivo* steady-state kinetic calculations. Another example is the conversion of malic acid to fumaric acid. In this case, the actual free energy change is small; the two acids are essentially in equilibrium with respect to C^{14}-labeling. Thus the sum of the pools of the two acids can be treated from a labeling standpoint as a single entity.

In any event, if malic acid is not labeled by exchange and is not converted to succinic acid yet is being formed at a rapid rate under steady-state conditions, it must undergo some as-yet-unknown conversion. One possibility might be that it is split to give glyoxylic acid and free acetate. The actual free energy change for such a reaction under steady-state conditions would be negative, whereas the reaction to give glyoxylic acid and acetyl CoA would probably be positive and the latter reaction would not occur. Acetate could be converted to acetyl phosphate with ATP and then to acetyl CoA. The acetyl CoA thus formed could be used in fatty acid synthesis and other biosynthetic reactions. The glyoxylic acid could be used in the synthesis of glycolic acid, glycine, and possibly, as suggested in the previous section, glutamic acid.

The synthesis of labeled malic acid could occur via condensation of glyoxylate with acetyl CoA, provided there is some other route for the labeling of these two-carbon acids (such as are suggested later). It is quite likely that malic acid is so synthesized in the cytoplasm, outside the chloroplasts. Within the chloroplasts, however, the appearance of C^{14} in malic acid in the very shortest exposures to $C^{14}O_2$ and in the pre-illumination experiments (see Figure 5) indicate that it is, in part at least, a product of C_1-C_3 carboxylation and reduction.

Glycolic acid, acetic acid, and glyoxylic acid

Even if acetate and glyoxylate are formed from malic acid, there are probably other more important synthetic routes from the carbon reduction cycle to these compounds. Benson and Calvin (41) found that barley seedlings subjected to 30 seconds photosynthesis with $C^{14}O_2$, followed by 2 minutes light without CO_2, formed large amounts of C^{14}-labeled glycolic acid. Calvin et al. (14) and Schou et al. (42) degraded glycolic acid and phosphoglyceric acid obtained from barley leaves and from Scenedesmus that had photosynthesized for a few seconds in the presence of $C^{14}O_2$ or $HC^{14}O_3^-$. The alpha and beta carbon atoms of PGA were found to be always about equal to each other in radioactivity and always less than the carboxyl carbon until such time (1 to 5 minutes) as all three carbon atoms were completely labeled. The two carbon atoms of glycolic acid were always about equal to each other in labeling. When $C^{14}H_2OH$ —COOH was administered to the unicellular algae Scenedesmus during 10 minutes photosynthesis with $\frac{1}{2}$ per cent CO_2 in air or N_2, a pattern of photosynthetic intermediates was found similar to that obtained during photosynthesis with $C^{14}O_2$. Moreover, upon degradation of the PGA we found that less than 10 per cent of the radioactivity was in the carboxyl carbon. Clearly, glycolic acid is incorporated for the most part into normal intermediates of the carbon reduction cycle without preliminary conversion to CO_2, since so little C^{14} was found in the carboxyl carbon of PGA. However, alpha and beta carbon atoms of the PGA were found to be equally labeled. Thus the pathway from glycolic acid to the alpha and

39

beta carbon atoms of PGA involves a randomization of the label. This could mean that along this pathway there is a symmetrical intermediate or that an intermediate is in rapid reversible equilibrium with a symmetrical compound (see Figure 7).

When Wilson and Calvin (19) studied the effect of CO_2 depletion following a period of photosynthesis with $C^{14}O_2$ by algae, they found that the lowering of CO_2 pressure resulted in a great increase in the amount of labeled glycolic acid. This increase in labeled glycolic acid was sustained for at least 10 minutes. Upon application of 1 per cent CO_2 again, the level of labeled glycolic acid declined.

Tolbert (22) found that glycolic acid formation from $C^{14}O_2$ during 10 minutes photosynthesis in leaves of *Sedum alboresum* is much higher at very low CO_2 pressure than at high CO_2 pressure. As mentioned earlier, he also found that glycolic acid is the predominant labeled compound excreted into the medium by chloroplasts from Swiss chard photosynthesizing in the presence of $HC^{14}O_3^-$. He had shown earlier (43) that glycolic labeled with C^{14} is excreted into the medium by Chlorella photosynthesizing in $C^{14}O_2$. He suggested that glycolate may function in ion balance with HCO_3^- between cells and their medium or between chloroplasts and other cell compartments. He also proposed that glycolate might be a carrier of "carbohydrate reserves" from the chloroplasts to the cytoplasm.

Moses and Calvin (44) exposed photosynthesizing *Chlorella pyrenoidosa* to tritium-labeled water for various periods from 5 seconds to 3 minutes. Analysis was made by the usual extraction, two-dimensional paper chromatography, and radioautography. The greatest darkening of the film by far occurred where it was in contact with the glycolic acid area of the chromatogram. This result, which we shall discuss later, seems to agree with Tolbert's suggestion that the glycolic acid acts as a carrier of hydrogen.

During normal photosynthesis (Figure 2), two-carbon moieties (carbon atoms number 1 and 2 from a keto sugar phosphate) are transferred during a reaction similar to that catalyzed by transketolase (45,46) to an aldo-sugar phosphate, producing a new ketose phosphate, two carbon atoms longer than the starting aldose. Other enzymes have been found in nonphotosynthetic organisms which convert the carbon atoms number 1 and 2 of a ketose phosphate to acetyl phosphate, leaving the remainder of the sugar as an aldose phosphate. One of these is phosphoketolase (47), which is specific for xylulose-5-phosphate, while another is fructose-6-phosphate ketolase (48), which can act on either fructose-6-phosphate or xylulose-5-phosphate. These enzymes require thiamine pyrophosphate, inorganic phosphate and, in some cases, Mg^{++}. Stimulation by Mn^{++} or Ca^{++} in place of Mg^{++} could sometimes be observed, whereas levels of Mn above 10^{-3} were inhibitory.

Breslow has proposed a mechanism for the role of thiamine pyrophosphate in these reactions (49,50). In his mechanism, some of which forms the basis for part of Figure 7, the hydrogen at position 2 of the thiazole ring is an active hydrogen which can dissociate from the acidic carbon at that position to give a carbanion. This carbanion adds to the carbonyl carbon of the ketose (somewhat analogous to cyanhydrin addition). The bond between carbons 2 and 3 of the ketose breaks, with the electron pair going to the reduction of carbon 2 of the ketose, to give a glycolaldehyde-thiamine pyrophosphate. The remainder of the sugar becomes an aldose. Reversal of this reaction path, with a different aldose, completes the transketolase reaction.

Alternatively, glycolaldehyde-thiamine pyrophosphate may eliminate the elements of water (OH^- from the beta carbon and H^+ from the alpha carbon of the glycolaldehyde moiety) to give the enol form and thence the keto form of acetyl-ThPP. This compound can undergo phosphoroclastic cleavage to give acetyl phosphate and thiamine pyrophosphate (ThPP).

The mechanisms find support in the demonstration by Breslow that the hydrogen atom on the number 2 position

41

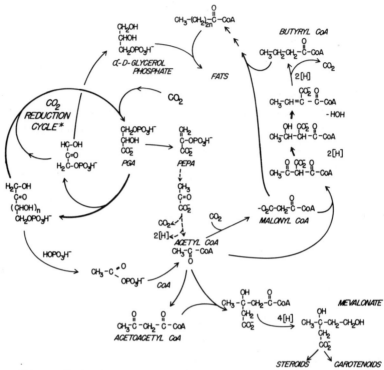

Figure 7. Pathways from carbon reduction cycle to acetyl phosphate and glycolic acid. For details of the carbon reduction cycle, see Figure 2.

of the thiazole ring does exchange rapidly in D_2O (49). In support of an analogous mechanism for the role of ThPP in the oxidation of pyruvate, Krampitz and co-workers (51, 52) synthesized the postulated intermediate, an acetaldehyde-ThPP compound with the acetaldehyde bonded to the number 2 carbon atom of the thiazole ring as an alpha hydroxyethyl group. This compound was found to be active in the reactivation of carboxylase and also to be capable of non-enzymatic reaction with acetaldehyde to give acetoin. The postulated mechanism for the oxidation of pyruvic acid thus begins with a reaction between pyruvate and ThPP to give addition of the carbonyl carbon to the thiazole-ring-position number 2. Concurrently or immediately following this addition, decarboxylation occurs to give acetaldehyde-ThPP. This compound reacts with oxidized lipoic acid to give acetyl dihydrolipoic acid, which in turn reacts with CoA to give dihydrolipoic acid and acetyl CoA (53–56).

Wilson and Calvin (19), following their observation of glycolate accumulation at low CO_2 pressure, suggested that the glycolyl moiety transferred by transketolase is the source of glycolic acid. We should now like to suggest specifically that the glycolaldehyde-ThPP compound formed in the first step of the transketolase or phosphoketolase reactions may undergo oxidation to give glycolyl CoA and, eventually, glycolate. This oxidation need not follow a pathway exactly analogous to the oxidation of acetaldehyde-ThPP, but we have shown it so in Figure 7.

As mentioned earlier, during photosynthesis glycolate can be converted to the alpha and beta carbon atoms of PGA via carbon atoms 1 and 2 of the pentose in the carbon reduction cycle. Thus it appears that the pathway from pentose phosphate to glycolate and glyceraldehyde phosphate should be reversible. The incorporation of glycolate via such a pathway would require an energy input, probably in the form of an activation by ATP. Finally, some state in the incorporation pathway should involve equilibration with a symmetric intermediate because administration of glycolate-2-C^{14} to photosynthesizing plants leads to PGA labeled equally in the alpha and beta carbon atoms. We have indicated one such symmetric compound and there may be other possibilities.

The formation of glycolyl CoA and reduced lipoic acid as shown in Figure 7 are hypothetical. If glycolyl CoA were formed, it seems likely that it would be an important intermediate in paths as yet unknown. In any event, if there is any conversion of carbon atoms number 1 and 2 of ketose to glycolic acid during photosynthesis, then an oxidation of the glycolyl fragment is required so that some cofactor, although not necessarily lipoic acid, must be reduced.

Let us now attempt to explain the observation that

labeled glycolate accumulates during photosynthesis with $C^{14}O_2$ when the CO_2 pressure is reduced.

1. Enzyme systems present in chloroplasts can bring about the oxidation of glycolate to glyoxylate with oxygen and the reduction of glyoxylate to glycolate with DPNH (57). If some steady-state relation between these two acids exists, it might well be shifted toward more glycolate at low CO_2 pressures by the increase in the ratio of DPNH/DPN+ that would result from the decreased utilization of TPNH for the carbon reduction cycle. Moreover, the oxidation of glycolate by O_2 must in fact be limited in rate during photosynthesis, or glycolate would not be seen at all. Possibly glycolate is more effectively oxidized by some intermediate hydroxyl or peroxide involved in the liberation of oxygen following the splitting of water during the primary act in photosynthesis. If so, such an intermediate oxidant may decrease in concentration at low CO_2 pressure because of recombination with primary reductant that would build up, again as a result of decreased utilization by the carbon reduction cycle. A decrease in the oxidant concentration would reduce the oxidation of glycolate.

2. Low CO_2 pressure might result in higher pH inside the chloroplasts. The phosphoketolase reaction, leading to acetyl CoA and involving the removal of OH^- from glycolaldehyde-ThPP, might be blocked, and the oxidation of the glycolaldehyde-ThPP to glycolyl CoA might be favored.

3. If glycolyl CoA is formed and is a biosynthetic intermediate, the reactions in which it is used might require CO_2 analogous to the conversion of acetyl CoA to malonyl CoA in fatty acid biosynthesis. Low CO_2 pressure could thus lead to an increased concentration of glycolyl CoA and permit its more rapid hydrolysis to glycolate.

Tanner and co-workers (58,59) have recently proposed a direct route from CO_2 to glycolic acid during photosynthesis. According to his scheme, CO_2 is reduced by TPNH and $MnCl^-$ to the radical $CHO\cdot$. Two of these $CHO\cdot$ radicals are then condensed to give glyoxal, thence glycolic acid.

44

This glycolic acid is then oxidized by 2 molecules of $MnCl(OH)_2$ (produced in the first step) to give glyoxylic acid. According to Tanner, the greater labeling of glycolic acid at low CO_2 pressure during photosynthesis with $C^{14}O_2$ is due to the first step being first order with respect to the utilization of CO_2 and the production of trivalent manganese, whereas the second step is second order with respect to the utilization of trivalent manganese.

Whether or not Tanner's suggested route from CO_2 to glycolic acid will be borne out by experiment remains to be seen. In all our experiments with $C^{14}O_2$, labeled glycolic acid has been a relatively minor product of the photosynthesis, except in those cases where the CO_2 pressure has been permitted to drop to a very low level. Glycolic acid is somewhat volatile, but it is a curious characteristic of this compound on paper chromatograms that, although 20 to 85 per cent may evaporate from the paper during development of the chromatogram, the remainder disappears only very slowly from the papers. This statement is based on measurement of radioactivity following chromatography of synthetic C^{14}-labeled glycolic acid. Thus it would seem that if a pathway leading directly from CO_2 to glycolic acid (that is, with no isolable intermediates) were quantitatively important, we should have seen much more labeled glycolic acid following short periods of photosynthesis with $C^{14}O_2$. It could be that, under normal conditions of photosynthesis (say with 1 per cent CO_2 in air), the reservoir size or concentration of glycolic acid is very small, so that it would not appear to be strongly labeled, even though carbon from $C^{14}O_2$ enters it very rapidly.

However, Moses and Calvin (44) conducted parallel experiments (3 minutes photosynthesis by Chlorella in the presence of $C^{14}O_2$ in one case and T_2O in the other). The tritium-labeled glycolic acid accounted for more than 50 per cent of the darkening of the radioautograph in the subsequent analysis by chromatography, whereas in the parallel experiment the glycolic acid contained less than 5 per cent of all the C^{14} found in compounds on the chromatograph. Thus the incorporation of hydrogen into nonexchangeable positions on glycolic acid seems to occur at ten times or more the rate of incorporation of C^{14} into the same compound. The simplest interpretation is that glycolic acid plays a much more important role in the transport of hydrogen or reducing power than it does as an intermediate in carbon-compound formation from CO_2. If any carbon dioxide is reduced directly to glycolic acid during photosynthesis by Chlorella, it would seem to be a minor part of the total.

A special role for glycolic acid in hydrogen transport is suggested by a combination of experimental findings from several laboratories. To Moses' finding of extremely rapid tritium labeling of glycolic acid and Tanner's implication of the role of glycolic acid with the requirement for manganese, we may add Delavin and Benson's report (60) of the light stimulation of the oxidation of glycolic acid with O_2 to glyoxylate and peroxide in isolated chloroplasts. Further, we must mention that manganese is thought by Kessler (61) to play some part in the formation of peroxide or O_2 from water during the early stages of photosynthesis. Some form of peroxide is commonly postulated as an intermediate between water and O_2 during photosynthesis, and it may be that the plant has some mechanism for conserving the chemical potential energy that would be lost if peroxide were permitted to decompose to water and oxygen by a catalase mechanism.

The decrease in labeled glycolate in algae grown in Mn^{++}-deficient media (58,59) may be due to (1) some increase in the level of an intermediate in the oxygen-evolution pathway which is also capable of oxidizing glycolate to glyoxylate (presumably Mn^{++} might be required for the breakdown of this oxidant to O_2); (2) a decrease in reduced pyridine nucleotide concentration, owing to impairment of the oxygen-evolving pathway; or (3) some enzymic requirement for Mn^{++} in the biosynthetic pathway from glycolaldehyde-ThPP to glycolate.

Points (1) and (2) are related to the mechanisms suggested earlier for the effect of low CO_2 pressure on glycolate concentration.

Acetate

As shown in Figure 7, acetyl phosphate can be formed from the carbon reduction cycle via the phosphoketolase pathway. This involves dehydration of the ThPP-acetaldehyde compound derived from carbon atoms 1 and 2 of ketose phosphates. This route is especially attractive as a photosynthetic pathway, since it conserves chemical energy and requires no oxidation or decarboxylation. Known enzyme systems would readily convert the acetyl phosphate to acetyl CoA for fatty acid photosynthesis.

Another pathway from the carbon reduction cycle to acetyl CoA could be via oxidative decarboxylation of pyruvic acid. This reaction is of the type we have earlier viewed as unlikely in photosynthesizing chloroplasts on grounds of economy. However, this economy takes on a different aspect if one considers the rapid formation of alanine, which we believe might be a reductive amination of phosphoenolpyruvic acid derived from the carbon cycle (30). Our experiments indicate that about one-third of all NH_4^+ uptake occurs via this route. The resulting alanine must be used to a considerable extent in transamination reactions, resulting in the production of pyruvic acid. Although pyruvic acid is not labeled soon enough after the introduction of $C^{14}O_2$ to photosynthesizing plants to permit us to consider it a precursor to alanine, it does become slowly labeled at later times. Thus pyruvic acid could be a product of transamination from alanine. The slow labeling of pyruvate may be because alanine has a very large reservoir, which does not saturate with C^{14} for some minutes. Once formed, the pyruvic acid cannot

47

easily be converted back to PEPA. Rather, it must either go to malic acid via reductive carboxylation or be oxidized to acetyl CoA and CO_2.

The light-dark transient effect in $C^{14}O_2$ uptake during photosynthesis has often been observed (16,20). When the light is turned off, following a period of photosynthesis of algae with $C^{14}O_2$, labeled glutamic acid and citric acid accumulate. One explanation of this effect has been given, based on the proposed formation of acetyl CoA by pyruvic acid oxidation. Lipoic acid in its oxidized form is required to accept the electrons in this oxidation. It was suggested that while the light is on this cofactor is kept mostly in its reduced state, dihydrolipoic acid. The reduced cofactor could not promote pyruvic acid oxidation. When the light is turned off and reducing power is no longer generated, the oxidized form of lipoic acid would be made, and the oxidation leading to acetyl CoA would occur. Subsequent reactions, via the glyoxylate cycle, would then produce citric and glutamic acids.

However, if acetyl phosphate is formed by phosphoketolase during photosynthesis, a different explanation can be made. If we suppose that acetyl phosphate is still formed via phosphoketolase just after turning off the light, it will tend to accumulate. No reducing power or ATP is available for synthesis of fatty acids in the dark inside the chloroplasts. Therefore, acetyl phosphate will break down to free acetate, which will diffuse out of the chloroplast into the cytoplasm. There it will be used, via the glyoxylate cycle, in the synthesis of glutamic acid (62).

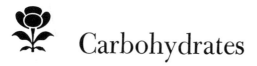 Carbohydrates

Monosaccharides

The carbon reduction cycle (Figure 2) includes as intermediate compounds the following sugar phosphates: 3-phosphoglyceraldehyde, dihydroxyacetone phosphate, fructose-1,6-diphosphate, fructose-6-phosphate, erythrose-4-phosphate, sedoheptulose-1,7-diphosphate, sedoheptulose-7-phosphate, xylulose-5-phosphate, ribulose-5-phosphate, ribose-5-phosphate, and ribulose-1,5-diphosphate. Besides these compounds, glucose phosphates are found to be very rapidly labeled in all plants in which we have studied the photosynthesis of carbon compounds from $C^{14}O_2$. When characterized, both glucose-6-phosphate and glucose-1-phosphate have been found. Other sugars found to be labeled somewhat more slowly in these experiments and identified as the free sugars following hydrolysis of the sugar monophosphate area include mannose and galactose.

In virtually all the studies of the labeled products of the photosynthesis of carbon compounds from $C^{14}O_2$ there has been found a striking absence of unphosphorylated monosaccharides (14). This is hardly surprising, since photosyn-

49

thesizing chloroplasts form phosphorylated sugars as intermediates in the carbon reduction cycle, since there is an abundance of ATP in the chloroplasts and since most known transformations of monosaccharides require phosphorylated forms of the sugars. Transformation of the phosphorylated sugars to the free sugars would for the most part result in a waste of chemical energy, for the sugar would then usually have to be phosphorylated again in reactions requiring ATP or UTP. Only when it becomes necessary to form a molecule that can be transported through the chloroplast membrane is it likely that a free sugar of relatively small molecular weight such as sucrose would be produced.

A listing of various enzyme systems that appear to be responsible for the carbon reduction cycle has been delayed until now, since many of these biochemical steps are of interest in a discussion of carbohydrate synthesis. In Table 2 there are listed the enzymes reported in the literature which appear to be responsible for steps of the carbon reduction cycle (Figure 2). Table 3 lists other enzymes which could account for subsequent steps in the synthesis of carbohydrates found to be labeled following relatively short periods of photosynthesis of algae with $C^{14}O_2$.

We wish to emphasize that the finding of an enzyme in plant tissue does not, of course, prove that that particular reaction goes on in the photosynthesizing chloroplast either at all or in precisely the same way that it has been found to occur *in vitro*. Moreover, we would not consider the isolation of an enzyme with high catalytic activity a necessary condition for believing that a given reaction may occur *in vivo*. The organization of the intact chloroplast inside the living cell and replete with all necessary *natural* cofactors and enzymes is such that some steps which occur *in vivo* may prove extremely difficult to demonstrate in cell-free systems. Nonetheless, the isolation of a cell-free system, capable of carrying out a reaction that has been suspected on the basis of *in vivo* studies, is important corroborative evidence.

The various enzymes listed in Tables 2 and 3, if present

Table 2

Plant-Tissue Enzymes That Catalyze Photosynthetic Reactions or Similar Reactions

Enzyme	No.	Reaction [a]	Plant material	Investigator (first author)
Carboxydismutase				
"Carboxylating enzyme"	1	$CO_2 + RuDP + H_2O \rightarrow 2\ 3\text{-PGA}$	*Chlorella*; spinach leaves, etc.	Quayle (63), Mayaudon (64), Weissbach (65–67), Jakoby (68), Racker (69)
Phosphoglyceryl kinase	2	$3\text{-PGA} + ATP \rightarrow 1,3\text{-DPGA}$	Pea seeds	Axelrod (6)
Triose phosphate dehydrogenase	3	$1,3\text{-DPGA} + TPNH \rightarrow Gl3P + TPN^+ + Pi$	Sugar beet leaves; green, tissues of several algae and higher plants	Arnon (7,70), Rosenberg (71), Stumpf (9,10), Fuller (72)
Triose phosphate isomerase	4	$Gl3P \rightarrow DHAP$	Pea seeds	Tewfic (73)
Aldolase	5	$Gl3P + DHAP \rightarrow FDP$	Pea seeds	Stumpf (9), Tewfic (74)
	6	$E4P + DHAP \rightarrow S7P$	Pea seeds	Hough (75)
Phosphatase	7	$FDP + H_2O \rightarrow F6P + Pi$	Spinach	Racker (76,77)
	8	$SDP + H_2O \rightarrow S7P + Pi$	Spinach	Racker (76,77)
Transketolase	9	$F6P + Gl3P \rightarrow E4P + Xu5P$	Spinach	Horecker (45)
	10	$S7P + Gl3P \rightarrow R5P + Xu5P$	Spinach	Horecker (45)
Ribulose phosphate–xylulose phosphate isomerase	11	$Ru5P \rightarrow Xu5P$	Yeast	Srere (78)
Phosphoribulokinase	12	$Ru5P + ATP \rightarrow RuDP + ADP$	Spinach	Hurwitz (79), Weissbach (80)

[a] Abbreviations: DHAP = dihydroxyacetone phosphate; E4P = erythrose-4-phosphate; FDP = fructose-1,6-diphosphate; F6P = fructose-6-phosphate; Gl3P = glyceraldehyde-3-phosphate; Pi = inorganic phosphate; 1,3DPGA = phosphoglyceryl-3-phosphate; R5P = ribose-5-phosphate; RuDP = ribulose-1,5-diphosphate; Ru5P = ribose-5-phosphate; SDP = sedoheptulose-1,7-diphosphate; S7P = sedoheptulose-7-phosphate; Xu5P = xylulose-5-phosphate.

Table 3

Some Plant-Tissue Enzymes That May Catalyze Reactions for Photosynthetic Formation of Carbohydrates (beyond the Carbon Reduction Cycle)

Enzyme	No.	Reaction[a]	Plant material	Investigator (first author)
Phosphohexose isomerase	13	F6P → G6P	*Phaseolus radiatus*	Ramasarma (81)
Phosphoglucomutase	14	G6P + Pi-enzyme → GDP + enzyme	Broadbean seeds	Morita (82),
		GDP → G1P + Pi-enzyme		Sidbury (83)
UDPG-pyrophosphorylase	15	G1P + UTP → UDPG + PP	Mung bean seedlings	Ginsberg (84)
UDPG-fructose-6-phosphate transglycosylase	16	UDPG + F6P → sucrose + UDP	Wheat germ	Leloir (85)
Sucrose phosphatase	17	SuP + H$_2$O → sucrose + Pi	Mung bean seedlings	Neufeld (86)
UDPG-4-epimerase (galactowaldenase)	18	UDPG → UDPGal	Mung bean seedlings	Neufeld (86),
		UTP + sugar-1-phosphate → UDPsugar + PP		Kalckar (87)

[a] Abbreviations (see also Table 2): GDP = glucose-1,6-diphosphate; G6P = glucose-6-phosphate; PP = pyrophosphate; SuP = sucrose phosphate; UDPGal = uridine diphosphogalactose; UDPG = uridine diphosphoglucose; UTP = uridine triphosphate.

in chloroplasts, could account for virtually all the monosaccharide phosphates found to be significantly labeled with C^{14} following a period of photosynthesis with $C^{14}O_2$ for several minutes in algae. Presumably there is present also another phosphohexose isomerase which catalyzes the conversion of fructose-6-phosphate to mannose-6-phosphate.

Among the enzyme systems listed in Table 3 are several that utilize sugar nucleotides in the biosynthetic conversion of sugars. Such systems have been widely studied and have been discussed and reviewed elsewhere (88–90). Hassid and co-workers have widely studied the interconversions of sugars by these systems in higher plants and have summarized the interrelations of many of these systems in plants (91). Certain of these systems, which appear in Table 3, are particularly active in the early labeling of sugars in plants photosynthesizing with $C^{14}O_2$ and must be mentioned here, if only briefly.

Buchanan et al. (15) identified uridine diphosphate glucose (UDPG) and uridine diphosphate galactose (UDPGal) in algae and found that the hexose moieties of these compounds were labeled with C^{14} during short periods of $C^{14}O_2$ photosynthesis even before sucrose. Thus the galactose found to be labeled in some experiments may be formed by the UDPG-UDPGal system.

Disaccharides and polysaccharides

As already indicated, when *Chlorella pyrenoidosa* photosynthesizes in the presence of $C^{14}O_2$, sucrose is the first free sugar to be labeled to any extent. Benson (92) found that the radiocarbon in the fructose moiety of the sucrose, following photosynthesis of $C^{14}O_2$ by Chlorella, Scenedesmus, and soybean leaves, was greater than the radioactivity in the glucose moiety. Moreover, the difference between fructose and glucose became greater as the time of photosynthesis was decreased. The prior labeling of the fructose indicated that the glucose phosphate used in the synthesis of sucrose is formed from fructose phosphate.

53

A study of the phosphorylated products of short-term photosynthesis in $C^{14}O_2$ led to the discovery of a sucrose phosphate (93). The "hexose monophosphates" produced during photosynthesis in $C^{14}O_2$ were treated with an invertase-free phosphatase preparation and subjected to paper chromatography. Although in most cases there were only minute traces of sucrose formed by this treatment, in sugar beet (5 minutes in $C^{14}O_2$) there was an appreciable quantity. It was identified by cochromatography and enzymic hydrolysis to glucose and fructose.

When this "hexose monophosphate" sample was subjected to chromatography in t-butanol:picric acid:water, radioactive areas corresponding to glucose-6-phosphate, fructose-6-phosphate, sedoheptulose and mannose phosphates, and sucrose phosphate were obtained. The sucrose phosphate gave sucrose on phosphatase treatment, and on acid hydrolysis glucose and fructose phosphate were produced. The latter did not cochromatograph with fructose-6-phosphate.

It appeared that in sucrose synthesis in green plants there are two possible mechanisms. Glucose-1-phosphate might react with fructose-1-phosphate to give sucrose phosphate, which would be dephosphorylated to sucrose. Alternatively, sucrose phosphate synthesis might be envisaged to occur through uridine diphosphate glucose (15), which becomes labeled shortly before sucrose in kinetic experiments with $C^{14}O_2$ (18). The uridine diphosphate glucose may be formed from glucose-1-phosphate by a UDPG pyrophosphorylase (reaction 15, Table 3). This pathway is shown in Figure 8 along with other pathways that may very likely occur during photosynthesis of carbohydrates from CO_2.

Leloir and Cardini (85) have isolated from wheat germ what appears to be two systems, one that catalyzes the reaction of fructose plus UDPG to give sucrose plus UDP, and a second that catalyzes the reaction UDPG plus fructose-6-phosphate to give sucrose phosphate plus UDP. Burma and Mortimer (94) have reported that with excised sugar beet leaves and leaf homogenates radioactive UDPG and sucrose

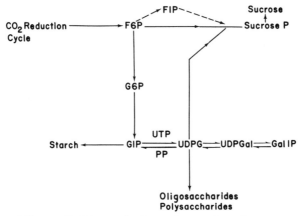

Figure 8. Biosynthetic pathways for photosynthesis of carbohydrates.

were formed when radioactive glucose-1-phosphate, fructose-6-phosphate, and UTP were added. They propose a mechanism identical to that postulated by Buchanan except for the choice of fructose-6-phosphate as the precursor instead of fructose-1-phosphate.

Not much is known about the formation of other polysaccharides. There is a rapid labeling of unidentified polysaccharides during photosynthesis with $C^{14}O_2$. On the usual two-dimensional chromatogram, developed as described earlier, these compounds form what appears to be a homologous series of polyglucoses extending from the origin nearly to sucrose. The compound of this series closest to sucrose has been hydrolyzed and found to contain only glucose.

Fats

During photosynthesis by unicellular algae, it is not uncommon for as much as 30 per cent of the carbon dioxide taken up to be incorporated into fats. In Scenedesmus, for example, after 5 minutes in light in the presence of C^{14}-labeled carbon dioxide, 30 per cent of the fixed radioactivity is found in lipid materials. This incorporation of radiocarbon is greatly in excess of the rate of any synthesis that could take place in the dark and is an indication of the stimulation of fat production in the light. Fat synthesis requires a greater number of equivalents of reducing agents than does synthesis of carbohydrate or protein. Moreover, the composition of the chloroplasts includes a very high proportion of fat material. Since there is an abundance of reduced cofactors and ATP in the chloroplast, and since the end product, fat, is needed in the chloroplast, it is likely that much fat synthesis takes place in the chloroplast and is therefore to be considered photosynthetic.

Fatty acids

All the well-known biosynthetic pathways to fatty acids require as a starting material acetate or acetyl CoA. We have already suggested under "Carboxylic Acids" four ways in which acetate, or acetyl CoA, could be made. These were: (1) splitting of malic acid to glyoxylate and acetate, (2) reduction of glycolic acid to acetate, (3) oxidation of pyruvic acid to acetyl CoA, and (4) dehydration and phosphoroclastic splitting the postulated glycolyl-enzyme complex from transketolase reaction of the carbon reduction cycle to give acetyl phosphate. We favor the last way as being the most likely. However, if only the first three of these pathways are available, the third is probably the most important.

However the acetate is formed, it is rapidly converted to fats in the light in algae. Experiments with Scenedesmus photosynthesizing in the presence of acetate-1-C^{14} and $C^{12}O_2$ (14) demonstrated a light-accelerated incorporation of acetate into fats. A similar light-enhanced incorporation of acetate-2-C^{14} into lipids by Euglena was found by Lynch and Calvin (95). Sissakian (96) demonstrated the synthesis of higher fatty acids from labeled acetate in chloroplasts from sunflower plants. The utilization of free acetate in the light by chloroplasts is to be expected, since there is an abundance of ATP in the photosynthesizing chloroplasts for the conversion of acetate to acetyl phosphate and thence to acetyl CoA.

The scheme of fatty acid synthesis proposed by Wakil and Ganguly (97) for the formation of fatty acids from acetyl CoA in animal tissues has been widely accepted. A similar pathway may exist in photosynthetic tissues. This pathway is incorporated in the hypothetical scheme of fat photosynthesis shown in Figure 9. Wakil (98) and Wakil and Ganguly (99) report that the first step in the synthesis from acetyl CoA is a carboxylation to give malonyl CoA. This step requires biotin and ATP, as well as Mn^{++}. Malonyl CoA and acetyl CoA then condense to give acetoacetyl CoA, which then undergoes a series of reductive steps to give eventually butyryl CoA and carbon dioxide (97).

Although the work of Ganguly and Wakil has been with animal tissues, it appears from the studies of Stumpf and co-workers (100–103) that similar systems of fatty acid syn-

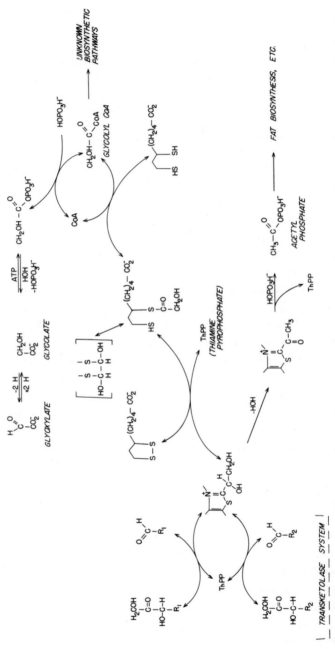

Figure 9. Some possible pathways of fat photosynthesis from CO_2. For details of the carbon reduction cycle, see Figure 2.

thesis exist in plant tissues. The early stages of fat synthesis may well be similar in photosynthesizing chloroplasts to those known for other plant tissue and animals. The later stages and the fat products formed during photosynthesis in chloroplasts are very likely different, since the chloroplast in all likelihood requires specialized fats for its operation. Benson and co-workers have identified a number of interesting compounds of glycerol phosphate and fatty acids as products of fat formation in green tissues. According to these workers, phosphatidyl glycerol is a major component of plant phospholipids. Moreover, they state that active transphosphatidyl action is observed during photosynthesis (104–106).

Glycerol phosphate

Alpha-D-glyceryl-1-phosphate is presumably formed in chloroplasts during photosynthesis by direct reduction with TPNH of dihydroxyacetone phosphate. This compound could then be further converted to the polyglycerol phosphates reported by Benson. The various glycerol phosphates would then presumably react with fatty acetyl CoA to produce fats. Some of these postulated biosynthetic routes are shown in Figure 9.

Pigments

Of major importance among the biosynthetic pathways of the chloroplast must be those leading to photosynthetic pigments. Although some of these may vary from one organism to another, all organisms must be capable of making at least one of the chlorophylls, carotenoids, and hematin pigments. During photosynthesis the simple precursor molecules for these synthetic paths are available from the carbon reduction cycle, whereas the reduced pyridine nucleotides and ATP are of course at high levels in the chloroplast.

Carotenoids and phytol

The starting point for the synthesis of carotenoids and phytol, as well as steroids and terpenes, is acetyl CoA. In the previous sections we discussed routes from the carbon reduction cycle to acetyl CoA. These are shown in Figures 7 and 9.

The biosynthetic paths to terpene compounds have been much clarified in recent years by work from the laboratories of Lynen (107), Bloch (108), Folkers (109), and Popjak (110). Successive condensations of acetyl CoA give acetoacetyl CoA and then β-hydroxy-β-methyl-glutaryl (or crotonyl)-CoA

(HMG-CoA). The HMG-CoA is then reduced to give mevalonic acid (Figure 9). Further steps along the biosynthetic path are shown in Figure 10. Pyrophosphorylation and decarboxylation of mevalonate give isopentenyl-pyrophosphate, the biological isoprene unit.

According to Lynen, isopentenyl-pyrophosphate units then condense to give, successively, C_{10}, C_{15}, and C_{20} compounds, as shown in Figure 10. Hydrogenation of the C_{20} compound could presumably lead to phytol, an alcohol that forms the phytyl tail of chlorophyll. Dimerization of the C_{15} compound, farnesyl pyrophosphate, gives squalene, the precursor for steroids. We might expect the C_{20} compound, geranylgeranyl pyrophosphate, to undergo a similar condensation to give C_{40} compounds, which could in turn be con-

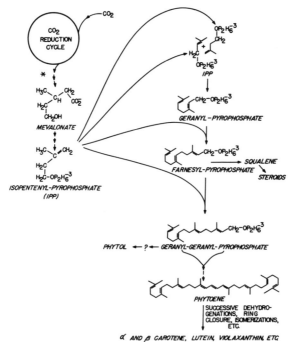

Figure 10. The biosynthesis of carotenoids. (* For details see Figures 7 and 9.)

verted to carotenoids. Stanier (111) has reported evidence indicating that the initial compound in this series is phytoene or tetrahydrophytoene (see Figure 10).

Present evidence indicates that conversion of the C_{40} compound formed from the condensation, to carotenoids, involves a number of dehydrogenations, and finally ring closure at the ends of the molecule. The various oxygen-containing carotenoid compounds are probably formed by oxidations, hydrations, etc. The structures of a great many of these compounds, both intermediates and end products, have been established in the laboratories of Karrer (112), Zechmeister (113), Inhoffen (114), Weedon (115), and others.

Chlorophyll and heme

The pathways to porphyrin compounds have been recently reviewed by Granick (116,117), Shemin (118), Rimington (119), and Bogorad (120). Some of the key steps from these paths are shown in Figure 11. Glycine and succinate formed from the carbon reduction cycle are the starting compounds for the syntheses of these pigments. Glycine may be formed from serine, which in turn is probably synthesized from 2-phosphoglycerate, formed from the 3-phosphoglycerate of the cycle (see the section on Amino Acids). Alternatively, glyoxylate may be transaminated to give glycine. The derivation of this glyoxylate from the carbon reduction cycle is not known for certain, but is probably related to the formation of glycolic acid (see the section on Carboxylic Acids). Thus glycolate formed by oxidation of the glycolyl fragment from the sugar phosphate transketolase system could be further oxidized to glyoxylic acid. A hypothetical split of malate could lead to acetate and glyoxylate.

If the chloroplast contained isocitritase, both succinate and glyoxylate could be formed by the same reaction on isocitrate. The isocitrate would in this case come from acetyl CoA and oxalacetate condensation, via citrate. Oxalacetate

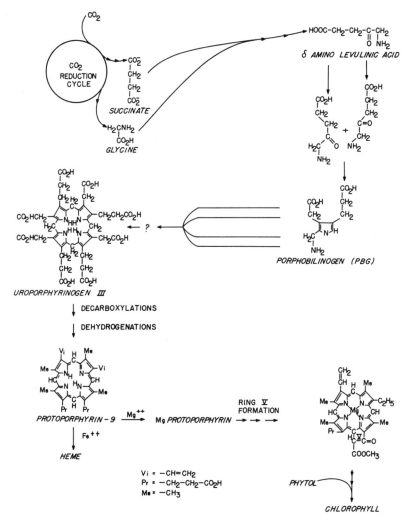

Figure 11. The biosynthesis of porphyrins.

is formed from the cycle by carboxylation of phosphoenolpyruvate, derived from phosphoglycerate.

Another, and perhaps more likely route to succinate is via reductive carboxylation to form malate, dehydration, and reduction of malate to give succinate.

63

As shown in Figure 11, condensation of glycine with succinic acid gives δ-amino levulinic acid, which in turn condenses with itself to make a substituted pyrrole ring (porphobilinogen). Condensations and isomerizations, the exact mechanisms of which are not known, lead to the formation of the tetrapyrrole structure of uroporphyrinogen(III) from four porphobilinogen molecules.

The conversion of uroporphyrinogen to protoporphyrin requires a number of decarboxylations of the substituent acyl groups, oxidation of two of these groups to vinyl groups, and dehydrogenation and aromatization of the pyrrole rings and the methylene bridges connecting them.

Protoporphyrin-9 is an important branching point: incorporation of Fe^{++} leads to heme and thence to the various hematin pigments, whereas incorporation of Mg^{++} ion leads ultimately to the synthesis of the chlorophylls. The latter pathway must first accomplish the formation of the fifth ring and the partial saturation of one of the pyrrole rings.

Finally the phytol alcohol, probably formed as shown in Figure 10, is attached to the pigment molecule as a phytyl group, and the synthesis of chlorophyll is complete. At some time, before or after this step, the alterations needed to make the various forms of chlorophyll, and to incorporate it into the structure of the photosynthetic apparatus are completed.

Aromatic nuclei

The shikimic acid pathway for the biosynthesis of aromatic compounds, including amino acids, from carbohydrates has been well established by the work of Davis (38) and his collaborators, who used biochemical mutants of *E. coli*. Without going into the details of this pathway, we may point out that the starting materials are phosphoenolpyruvate, which is readily available as a photosynthetic intermediate, and D-erythrose-4-phosphate, which is also an intermediate of the carbon reduction cycle. Presumably, therefore, the synthesis of aromatic amino acids in photosynthesizing plants would follow a pathway similar to the shikimic acid pathway. The first step in that pathway is the condensation of phosphoenolpyruvate with erythrose-4-phosphate to give a seven-carbon compound which has been identified as 2-keto-3-deoxy-D-araboheptonic acid-7-phosphate. This intermediate subsequently undergoes ring closure to give dehydroquinic acid. Rearrangements via a number of additional steps gives, eventually, phenylalanine and tyrosine. Higuchi (121) has summarized some of the reasons for believing that the shikimic acid pathway does occur in higher plants. For example, shikimic acid is of widespread occurence, and some of the enzymes of the pathway have in fact been found in higher plants. Neish (122) has further reviewed evidence for the shikimic acid pathway in plants.

Other
 biosynthetic
products

As we learn more about the capabilities of the chloroplast to form compounds from carbon during photosynthesis, we come closer to the conclusion that the chloroplast, as it exists in the living, undisturbed cell, is a self-sufficient factory capable of producing essentially all the materials required for its replenishment. Thus it appears to be able to make all kinds of sugars, polysaccharides, protein, fats, pigments, enzymes, and cofactors. In addition to this, it produces for export to the cytoplasm reserves of organic compounds. These are probably sugars, glycolic acid, and other neutral, relatively small, molecules which can be readily transported through the chloroplast membrane. Until more is known about the development and formation of chloroplasts, we cannot say just when it gains this complete synthetic ability. No doubt there are early stages in the development of chloroplasts in which it must be built from cytoplasmic materials derived in turn from already-functioning chloroplasts. There is no reason to suppose the chloroplast functions without nuclear control, even though it does not appear to have a nucleus of its own. Presumably it is possible for RNA molecules to move in and out of the chloroplast in some way. It cannot be said at the moment whether or not the chloroplast is capable of synthesizing nuclear material. It would seem likely, however, that the chloroplast can synthesize purines and pyrimidines, coenzymes, and nucleotide materials needed for the continued functioning of the chloroplast as a self-sufficient biosynthetic factory. If, as we now think, protein synthesis and enzyme synthesis occur in the chloroplast, then either the chloroplast must obtain a store of RNA molecules at its initial construction or else such molecules must be able to travel back and forth from the chloroplast to the cytoplasm.

In conclusion, we should say that the point of view of the ability of the chloroplast to carry out photosynthetic formation of many compounds is a departure from the view held only a few years ago. It was then thought that the primary function of photosynthesis was to form carbohydrate only. This carbohydrate was then thought to be used by the cytoplasm in the synthesis of all other compounds. Of course, the chloroplast must supply the carbohydrate and reducing power for the cytoplasmic synthesis. It now appears that chloroplasts also synthesize a complete spectrum of biochemical products, all of which might reasonably be considered to be photosynthetic products. Finally, as we learn more about the photosynthetic paths to these products, we are impressed not merely by their complexity but much more by the economy with which both energy and material are utilized.

References

1. Bassham, J. A., A. A. Benson, L. D. Kay, A. Z. Harris, A. T. Wilson, and M. Calvin, *J. Am. Chem. Soc.,* **76,** 1760 (1954).

2. Bassham, J. A., and M. Calvin, *The Path of Carbon in Photosynthesis,* Prentice-Hall, Inc., Englewood Cliffs, N.J., 1957.

3. Bassham, J. A., and M. Kirk, *Biochim. Biophys. Acta,* **43,** 447 (1960).

4. Norris, L. T., R. E. Norris, and M. Calvin, *J. Exptl. Botany,* **16,** 64 (1955).

5. Moses, V., and M. Calvin, *Proc. Natl. Acad. Sci. U.S.,* **44,** 260 (1958).

6. Axelrod, B., and R. S. Bandurski, *J. Biol. Chem.,* **204,** 939 (1953).

7. Arnon, D. I., *Science,* **116,** 635 (1952).

8. Gibbs, M., *Nature,* **170,** 164 (1952).

9. Stumpf, P. K., *J. Biol. Chem.,* **176,** 233 (1948).

10. Stumpf, P. K., *J. Biol. Chem.,* **182,** 261 (1950).

11. Stepka, W., A. A. Benson, and M. Calvin, *Science,* **108,** 304 (1948).

12. Benson, A. A., J. A., Bassham, M. Calvin, T. C. Goodale, V. A. Haas, and W. Stepka, *J. Am. Chem. Soc.,* **72,** 1710 (1950).

13. Bassham, J. A., A. A. Benson, and M. Calvin, *J. Biol. Chem.,* **185,** 787 (1950).

14. Calvin, M., J. A. Bassham, A. A. Benson, V. Lynch, C. Ouellet, L. Schou, W. Stepka, and N. E. Tolbert, *Symposia Soc. Exptl. Biol.,* **5,** 284 (1951).
15. Buchanan, J. G., V. Lynch, A. A. Benson, D. Bradley, and M. Calvin, *J. Biol. Chem.,* **203,** 935 (1953).
16. Calvin, M., and P. Massini, *Experientia,* **8,** 445 (1952).
17. Calvin, M., *Proc. Third Intern. Biochem. Congress,* Brussels, 1955, p. 211.
18. Benson, A. A., S. Kawaguchi, P. M. Hayes, and M. Calvin, *J. Am. Chem. Soc.,* **74,** 4477 (1952).
19. Wilson, A. T., and M. Calvin, *J. Am. Chem. Soc.,* **77,** 5948 (1955).
20. Bassham, J. A., K. Shibata, K. Steenberg, J. Bourdon, and M. Calvin, *J. Am. Chem. Soc.,* **78,** 4120 (1956).
21. Park, R. B., and N. G. Pon, *J. Mol. Biol.,* **3,** 1 (1961).
22. Tolbert, N. E., in *The Photochemical Apparatus: Its Structure and Function,* Brookhaven Symposia in Biology, Office of Technical Services, Department of Commerce, Washington, D.C., 1958, vol. 11, p. 271.
23. Aronoff, S., A. A. Benson, W. Z. Hassid, and M. Calvin, *Science,* **105,** 664 (1947).
24. Benson, A. A., M. Calvin, V. A. Haas, S. Aronoff, A. G. Hall, J. A. Bassham, and J. W. Weigl, in James Franck and W. E. Loomis (eds.), *Photosynthesis in Plants,* Iowa State College Press, Ames, 1949, pp. 381–401.
25. Nichiporovich, A. A., "Tracer Atoms Used to Study the Products of Photosynthesis as Depending on the Conditions in Which the Process Takes Place," *Proc. First Geneva Conf. on Peaceful Uses of Atomic Energy,* 1955.
26. Andreyeva, T. F., *Doklady Akad. Nauk SSSR,* **78,** 1033 (1951).
27. Voskrenskaya, N. R., *Doklady Akad. Nauk SSSR,* **93,** 911 (1953).
28. Nezgovorova, *Fiziol. Rastenii Akad. Nauk SSSR,* **6,** 451 (1959).
29. Sissakian, N. M., *Proc. Second Intern. Conf. on Peaceful Uses of Atomic Energy,* Geneva, 1958, Part 2, vol. 25, p. 159.
30. Smith, D. C., J. A. Bassham, and M. Kirk, *Biochim. Biophys. Acta,* **48,** 299 (1961).

31. Moses, V., O. Holm-Hansen, J. A. Bassham, and M. Calvin, *J. Mol. Biol.*, **1**, 21 (1959).

32. Van der Meulen, P. Y. F., and J. A. Bassham, *J. Am. Chem. Soc.*, **81**, 2233 (1959).

33. Holm-Hansen, O., N. G. Pon, K. Nishida, V. Moses, and M. Calvin, *Physiol. Plantarum*, **12**, 475 (1959).

34. Warburg, O., *Science*, **128**, 68 (1958).

35. Barker, H. A., R. M. Wilson, and A. Munch-Petersen, *Federation Proc.*, **16**, 151 (1957).

36. Munch-Petersen, A., and H. A. Barker, *J. Biol. Chem.*, **230**, 649 (1958).

37. Barker, H. A., R. D. Smith, R. M. Wilson, and H. Weissbach, *J. Biol. Chem.*, **234**, 320 (1959).

38. Davis, B. D., *Arch. Biochem. Biophys.*, **78**, 497 (1958).

39. Dekker, E. E., *Biochim. Biophys. Acta*, **40**, 174 (1960).

40. Virtanen, A. I., and P. K. Hietala, *Acta Chem. Scand.*, **9**, 175 (1955).

41. Benson, A. A., and M. Calvin, *J. Exptl. Botany*, **1**, 63 (1951).

42. Schou, L., A. A. Benson, J. A. Bassham, and M. Calvin, *Physiol. Plantarum*, **3**, 487 (1950).

43. Tolbert, N. E., and L. P. Zill, *J. Biol. Chem.*, **222**, 895 (1956).

44. Moses, V., and M. Calvin, *Biochim. Biophys. Acta*, **33**, 297 (1959).

45. Horecker, B. L., P. Z. Smyrniotis, and H. Klenow, *J. Biol. Chem.*, **205**, 661 (1953).

46. Racker, E., G. de la Haba, and I. G. Leder, *Arch. Biochem. Biophys.*, **48**, 238 (1954).

47. Heath, E. C., J. Hurwitz, B. L. Horecker, and A. Ginsburg, *J. Biol. Chem.*, **231**, 1009 (1958).

48. Schram, M., and E. Racker, *Nature*, **179**, 1349 (1957).

49. Breslow, R., *J. Am. Chem. Soc.*, **80**, 3179 (1958).

50. Breslow, R., *J. Cellular Comp. Physiol.*, **54**, Suppl. 1, 100 (1959).

51. Krampitz, L. O., *J. Cellular Comp. Physiol.*, **54**, Suppl. 1, 101 (1959).

52. Krampitz, L. O., G. Greull, C. S. Miller, J. B. Bicking, H. R. Skeggs, and J. M. Sprague, *J. Am. Chem. Soc.*, **80**, 5893 (1958).

53. Reed, L. J., B. D. DeBusk, I. C. Gunsalus, and C. S. Hornberger, Jr., *Science*, **114**, 63 (1951).

54. Reed, L. J., *Adv. in Enzymol.,* **18,** 319 (1956).
55. Gunsalus, I. C., L. S. Barton, and W. Gruber, *J. Am. Chem. Soc.,* **78,** 1763 (1956).
56. Gunsalus, I. C., in W. D. McElroy and B. Glass (eds.), *Mechanisms of Enzyme Action,* Johns Hopkins Press, Baltimore, 1951, Vol. I, p. 366.
57. Zelitch, I., and G. A. Barber, *Plant Physiol.,* **35,** 623 (1960).
58. Tanner, H. A., T. E. Brown, C. Eyster, and R. W. Treharne, *Ohio J. Sci.,* **60,** 231 (1960).
59. Tanner, H. A., T. E. Brown, C. Eyster, and R. W. Treharne, *Biochem. Biophys. Research Comm.,* **3,** 205 (1960).
60. Delavin, L. A., and A. A. Benson, *The Photochemical Apparatus: Its Structure and Function,* Brookhaven Symposia in Biology, Office of Technical Services, Department of Commerce, Washington, D.C., 1958, vol. 11, p. 259.
61. Kessler, E., in H. Gaffron et al. (eds.), *Research in Photosynthesis,* Interscience Publishers, Inc., New York, 1957, p. 243.
62. Kornberg, H. L., *Proc. Fourth Intern. Biochem. Congr.,* Vienna, 1958, vol. 13, p. 251.
63. Quayle, J. R., R. C. Fuller, A. A. Benson, and M. Calvin, *J. Am. Chem. Soc.,* **76,** 3610 (1954).
64. Mayaudon, J., A. A. Benson, and M. Calvin, *Biochim. Biophys. Acta,* **23,** 342 (1957).
65. Weissbach, A., and B. L. Horecker, *Federation Proc.,* **14,** 302 (1955).
66. Weissbach, A., B. L. Horecker, and J. Hurwitz, *J. Biol. Chem.,* **218,** 795 (1956).
67. Weissbach, A., P. Z. Smyrniotis, and B. L. Horecker, *J. Am. Chem. Soc.,* **76,** 3611 (1954).
68. Jakoby, W. G., D. O. Brummond, and S. Ochoa, *J. Biol. Chem.,* **218,** 811 (1956).
69. Racker, E., *Arch. Biochem. Biophys.,* **69,** 300 (1957).
70. Arnon, D. E., L. L. Rosenberg, and F. R. Whatley, *Nature,* **173,** 1132 (1954).
71. Rosenberg, L. L., and D. I. Arnon, *J. Biol. Chem.,* **217,** 361 (1955).
72. Fuller, R. C., and M. Gibbs, *Plant Physiol.,* **31,** xxxi (1956).
73. Tewfic, S., and P. K. Stumpf, *J. Biol. Chem.,* **192,** 519 (1951).
74. Tewfic, S., and P. K. Stumpf, *Am. J. Botany,* **36,** 567 (1949).

75. Hough, L., and J. K. N. Jones, *J. Chem. Soc.,* **1953,** 342.
76. Racker, E., *Nature,* **175,** 249 (1955).
77. Racker, E., and E. A. R. Schroeder, *Arch. Biochem. Biophys.,* **74,** 326 (1958).
78. Srere, P. A., J. R. Cooper, V. Klybas, and E. Racker, *Arch. Biochem. Biophys.,* **59,** 535 (1955).
79. Hurwitz, J., A. Weissbach, B. L. Horecker, and P. Z. Smyrniotis, *J. Biol. Chem.,* **218,** 769 (1956).
80. Weissbach, A., P. Z. Smyrniotis, and B. L. Horecker, *J. Am. Chem. Soc.,* **76,** 5572 (1954).
81. Ramasarma, T., and K. V. Giri, *Arch. Biochem. Biophys.,* **62,** 91 (1956).
82. Morita, S., S. Makamura, and T. Ito, *Ochanomizu Joshi Daigaku Shizenkagaku Hôkoku,* **4,** 68 (1955).
83. Sidbury, J. B., and V. A. Najjar, *J. Biol. Chem.,* **227,** 517 (1957).
84. Ginsberg, V., *J. Biol. Chem.,* **232,** 55 (1958).
85. Leloir, L. F., and C. E. Cardini, *J. Biol. Chem.,* **214,** 157 (1955).
86. Neufeld, E. F., V. Ginsberg, E. W. Putman, D. Fanshier, and W. Z. Hassid, *Arch. Biochem. Biophys.,* **69,** 602 (1957).
87. Kalckar, H. M., *Biochim. Biophys. Acta,* **12,** 250 (1953).
88. Leloir, L. F., *Proc. Third Intern. Biochem. Congr.,* Brussels, 1955, p. 154.
89. Baddiley, J., and J. G. Buchanan, *Quart. Revs. (London),* **12,** 152 (1958).
90. Kalckar, H. M., *Adv. in Enzymol.,* **20,** 111 (1958).
91. Hassid, W. Z., E. F. Neufeld, and D. S. Feingold, *Proc. Natl. Acad. Sci. U.S.,* **45,** 905 (1959).
92. Benson, A. A., *Arch. Biochem. Biophys.,* **32,** 223 (1951).
93. Buchanan, J. G., *Arch. Biochem. Biophys.,* **44,** 140 (1953).
94. Burma, D. P., and D. C. Mortimer, *Arch. Biochem. Biophys.,* **62,** 16 (1956).
95. Lynch, V. H., and M. Calvin, *Ann. N.Y. Acad. Sci.,* **56,** 890 (1953).
96. Sissakian, N. M., and B. P. Smirov, *Biokhimiya,* **21,** 275 (1956).
97. Wakil, S. J., and J. Ganguly, *J. Am. Chem. Soc.,* **81,** 2597 (1959).
98. Wakil, S. J., *J. Am. Chem. Soc.,* **80,** 6465 (1958).

99. Wakil, S. J., and J. Ganguly, *Federation Proc.*, **18**, 346 (1959).

100. Stumpf, P. K., *Federation Proc.*, **18**, 329 (1959).

101. Hatch, M. D., and P. K. Stumpf, Pacific Slope Biochemical Conference Abstract, Paper 28, 1960.

102. Mudd, J. B., and P. K. Stumpf, Pacific Slope Biochemical Conference Abstract, Paper 29, 1960.

103. Barron, E. J., and P. K. Stumpf, Pacific Slope Biochemical Conference Abstract, Paper 30, 1960.

104. Benson, A. A., and B. Maruo, *Biochim. Biophys. Acta,* **27,** 189 (1958).

105. Benson, A. A., J. F. G. Wintermans, and R. Wiser, *Plant Physiol.,* **34,** 315 (1959).

106. Benson, A. A., and E. H. Strickland, *Biochim. Biophys. Acta,* **41,** 328 (1960).

107. Lynen, F., B. W. Agranoff, H. Eggerer, U. Henning, and E. M. Moslein, *Angew. Chem.,* **71,** 657 (1959); Eggerer, H., and F. Lynen, *Ann. Chem. Liebigs,* **630,** 58 (1960).

108. Rilling, H. C., and K. Block, *J. Biol. Chem.,* **234,** 1424 (1959).

109. Folkers, K., C. H. Shunk, B. O. Linn, F. M. Robinson, P. E. Wittreich, J. W. Huff, J. L. Gilfillan, and H. R. Skeggs, *Ciba Foundation Symposium on Biosynthesis of Terpenes and Sterols,* J. A. Churchill, Ltd., London, 1959, Sec. 20.

110. Popjak, G., *Ciba Foundation Symposium on Biosynthesis of Terpenes and Sterols,* J. A. Churchill, Ltd., London, 1959, Sec. 148.

111. Stanier, R. Y., *Harvey Lectures,* **54,** 219 (1960).

112. Entschel, R., and P. Karrer, *Helv. Chim. Acta,* **42,** 466 (1959).

113. Zechmeister, L., *Fortschr. Chem. org. Naturstoffe,* **15,** 31 (1958); **18,** 223 (1960).

114. Inhoffen, H. H., and D. Erdmann, *Ann. Chem. Liebigs,* **598,** 51 (1956).

115. Akhtar, M., and B. C. L. Weedon, *J. Chem. Soc. (London),* **1959,** 4058; Davis, J. B., and B. C. L. Weedon, *Proc. Chem. Soc,* **1960,** 182.

116. Granick, S., *Proc. Fifth Intern. Biochem. Congr.,* Moscow, August 1961, Symposium VI, in press.

117. Granick, S., and D. Mauzerall, in D. M. Greenberg (ed.), *Chemical Pathways of Metabolism,* Academic Press, Inc., New York, 1961, vol. 2.

118. Shemin, D., *Ergeb. Physiol.* **49,** 299 (1957).

119. Rimington, C., *Ann. Rev. Biochem.*, **26,** 561 (1957).
120. Bogorad, L., in M. B. Allen (ed.), *Comparative Biochemistry of Photoreactive Systems,* Academic Press, Inc., New York, 1960, p. 227.
121. Higuchi, T., *Proc. Fourth Intern. Biochem. Congr.,* Vienna, 1958, vol. 2, p. 161.
122. Neish, A. C., *Ann. Rev. Plant Physiol.,* **11,** 55 (1960).

 Reprints

EXPERIENTIA VOL. VIII/12, 1952 – p. 445
VERLAG BIRKHÄUSER, BASEL/SCHWEIZ

The Path of Carbon in Photosynthesis[1]

(XX. The Steady State)

By M. Calvin and P. Massini[2], Berkeley, Cal.

Photosynthesis, the process by which green plants are able to capture electromagnetic energy in the form of sunlight and transform it into stored chemical energy in the form of a wide variety of reduced (relative to carbon dioxide) carbon compounds provides the only major source of energy for the maintenance and propagation of all life. For this and other reasons, the study of the nature of this process has been a very attractive area for many years and a wide variety of scientific interest and backgrounds have been brought to bear upon it. These range from the purely biological to the strictly physical with the biochemical and physicochemical area lying between. Important contributions to the understanding of the phenomenon have come from all these areas, but in spite of the enormous amount of work and study that has gone into the problem, relatively little is known, or rather understood, about the fundamental character of the process even today. It is perhaps pardonable that one engaged in studies in this area tends to the conclusion that most of the knowledge has been acquired in the relatively recent past. Discounting that tendency, it still seems fair to say that we have only just begun in the last decade or so to gain some understanding of the intimate details by which the basic process represented in the overall reaction

$$CO_2 + H_2O \xrightarrow[-\text{Energy}]{+\,h\upsilon} O_2 + (CH_2O)_x$$

has come to be understood. The recognition of this overall reaction as written, to represent the basic nature of the process of photosynthesis, and, further, that its reversal represents the basic reaction of respiration is, of course, an old one.

As a result of more recent study, it has been possible to separate the process of photosynthesis into two distinct and separate parts. The general features of this

separation may be represented in the following chart (Fig. 1). The essential feature of the separation is the independence of the photochemical part of photosynthesis from the carbon dioxide reduction part. We shall not here even try to outline all of the various forms of evidence which have been adduced in support of such a scheme but only to point out additional bits which have been added in recent years and particularly those which stem from our own work[1].

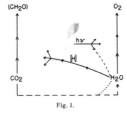

Fig. 1.

The scheme itself is an outgrowth of proposals of some fifteen years ago by Van Niel[2] resulting from his studies of the comparative biochemistry of photosynthesis. More recently, the photochemical apparatus has been shown to be separable from the rest of the plant by the experiments of Hill[3].

He was able to make preparations of chloroplasts and chloroplastic fragments which, upon illumination in the presence of suitable oxidizing agents other than carbon dioxide, were able to evolve molecular oxygen. Still more recently, Ochoa an others[4] were able to demonstrate that these same preparations were capable of using coenzyme I and II (D.P.N. and T.P.N.) as

[1] The work described in this paper was sponsored by the U.S. Atomic Energy Commission.
[2] Radiation Laboratory and Department of Chemistry, University of California, Berkeley. Fellow of the Swiss Foundation, «Stiftung für Stipendien auf dem Gebiete der Chemie», 1951–1952.

[1] M. Calvin and A. A. Benson, Science 107, 476 (1948). – A. A. Benson and M. Calvin, Cold Spring Harbor Symp. quant. Biol. 13, 6 (1948). – M. Calvin and A. A. Benson, Science 109, 140 (1949).
[2] C. B. Van Niel, Photosynthesis in Plants, Chapter 22 (Iowa State College Press, Ames, Iowa, 1949), pp. 437–495.
[3] R. Hill, Nature 139, 881 (1947); Proc. roy. Soc. (London) [B] 127, 192 (1939).– R. Hill and R. Scarisbrick, Nature 146, 61 (1940).
[4] W. Vishniac and S. Ochoa, J. Biol. Chem. 195, 75 (1952). – D. I. Arnon, Nature 167, 1008 (1951). – L. J. Tolmach, Arch. Biochem. Biophys. 33, 120 (1951).

suitable oxidizing agents leading to the evolution of oxygen. Furthermore, the experiments of Ruben[1] showed that the molecule of oxygen evolved in photosynthesis had its proximate origin in the oxygen of the water molecule and that the oxygen atom associated with the carbon dioxide must first pass through water before arriving at gaseous oxygen. From the chart it may be seen that the ultimate result, then, of·the photochemical reaction initiated by the absorption of light by the chlorophyll molecule is the division of the water molecule into an oxidized part which ultimately leads to molecular oxygen and some reduced parts represented in the chart by [H].

This reduced part [H] we have called "reducing power" because as yet it is not possible to state specifically what form or forms it may be in. This reducing power is capable of reducing carbon dioxide in the absence of light; that is to say, that the reduction of carbon dioxide itself is a dark reaction. This was indicated first in the earlier experiment of McAlister[2] in which he was able to show that following a period of photosynthesis a number of plants continued to absorb carbon dioxide for a short period (seconds to minutes) after cessation of illumination. We were able to demonstrate this in an even more direct and unequivocal fashion and generalize it for all plants so far tried when we were able to show that not only did all of these plants absorb quantities of carbon dioxide in the dark after illumination but that the products formed in the dark were qualitatively and under certain conditions quantitatively similar to those formed in a fairly comparable light period[3]. The method used for this demonstration was the same as those to be described later in the review. The lifetime in the dark of this reducing power which is generated by light is also of the order of seconds to minutes and almost certainly corresponds to a concentration of one or more definite chemical species. It is quite conceivable, as mentioned earlier, that some of it might be in the form of reduced coenzymes.

Very recently it has been reported[4] that both the higher plants and isolated chloroplasts emit a chemiluminiscence following cessation of illumination. This chemiluminiscence has a decay time which corresponds very closely to that which we have observed for the reducing power. In fact, it would seem almost surely to represent the reversal of the conversion of electromagnetic into chemical energy, namely, the transformation of at least some of the chemical energy stored in the reducing power into the electromagnetic energy of luminiscence. Furthermore, the luminiscence is re-

duced by the presence of carbon dioxide in those cases in which the carbon dioxide fixing system is still present. However, when the carbon dioxide system has been removed, as is true in the case of chloroplasts, the luminiscence becomes independent of carbon dioxide.

While it thus appears that the unique problem of photosynthesis lies in the right hand half of the·chart of Figure 1, the present discussion will be limited to the other side of the chart, that is, the path through which carbon passes on its way from carbon dioxide to all the raw materials of the plant. It is essentially a study of what we now believe to be entirely dark reactions and might best be characterized as phytosynthesis. This area not only has a great interest for its own sake but would almost certainly cast some light upon the nature of the reducing agents which arrive from the photochemical part of the reaction and drive the carbon cycle toward reduction. The reason for this particular interest lies in the fact that we have, in recent years, come into possession of a tool which is especially suited for this study, namely, labeled carbon atoms in the form of a radioactive isotope of carbon, C^{14}. All of the results that will be described later were made possible through the use of this labeled carbon dioxide. With such a labeled molecule available, the design of an experiment for determining the sequence of compounds into which the carbon atoms of carbon dioxide may pass during the course of their incorporation in the plant is, in its first phase, a straightforward one.

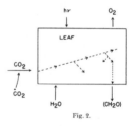

Fig. 2.

We may visualize the problem in terms of the chart in Figure 2 in which the green leaf is represented schematically as a closed opaque container into which stream the raw materials of photosynthesis, namely, carbon dioxide, light and water containing the necessary mineral elements. From this container are evolved the products of photosynthesis—oxygen gas and the reduced carbon compounds constituting the plant and its stored reserves. Heretofore, it has been possible to study in a quantitative way the nature of the process going on inside the opaque container only by varying external conditions and noting variations in the final products. Although there has been no serious doubt that the formation of sugar did not take place by the aggregation of six molecules of carbon dioxide, six

[1] S. Ruben, M. Randall, M. D. Kamen, and J. Hyde, J. Am. Chem. Soc. 63, 877 (1941).
[2] E. D. McAlister and J. Myers, J. Smithsonian Inst. Publ. (Misc. Coll.) 6, 99 (1940).
[3] M. Calvin, J. Chem. Education 26, 639 (1949).
[4] B. L. Strehler and W. Arnold, J. Gen. Physiol. 34, 809 (1951). – B. L. Strehler, Arch. Biochem. Biophys. 34, 239 (1951).

molecules of water and the requisite number of light quanta into a single unit followed by the rearrangement into hexose and molecular oxygen, no specific information was available as to the compounds which might act as intermediates. Assuming that such a chain of intermediates exists, it is quite clear that by setting up some photosynthetic organism, leaf or other suitable material, in a *steady state* of photosynthesis in which the various ingredients are being absorbed and products formed in some uniform manner and injecting the labeled carbon dioxide into the entering carbon dioxide stream, we should find the label appearing successively in time in that chain of intermediates. This can be observed by stopping the entire process after a suitable lapse of time and examining the incorporated labeled carbon to determine the nature of the compounds into which it has been built. It is also clear that in addition to the identity and sequence of the compounds into which the carbon is incorporated, we may also determine the order in which the various carbon atoms within each compound acquire the label. With this type of information at hand it should be possible to reconstruct the sequence of events from the time of entry of the carbon atom into the plant as carbon dioxide until it appears in the various more or less finished products of the plant.

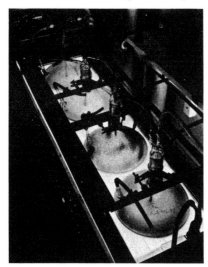

Fig. 3.—Algae Plant.

While photosynthetic experiments have been done with a vide variety of plant materials, the major kinetic work has been carried out with suspensions of unicellular green algae. The reason for this lies in the

Fig. 4.—"Lollipop".

fact that these algae may be obtained in a reproducible biological form relatively easily and in any amount. They are grown in the laboratory in a continuous culture arrangement shown in Figure 3. The algae may be harvested from these flasks daily or every other day, depending upon the type of material desired. Such cultures have been maintained in a continuous fashion over periods extending beyond several months. Most of our experiments have been performed with the unicellular green algae *Chlorella* or *Scenedesmus*. After harvesting the algae are washed with distilled water and resuspended in the medium in which the experiment is to be done. This suspension is placed in a flat vessel called a "lollipop", a photograph of which is shown in Figure 4. A stream of air containing carbon dioxide is passed through the algae while they are being illuminated so as to achieve a steady state of photosynthesis.

In order to begin the experiment the air stream is interrupted and the labeled bicarbonate is injected into the algal suspension. After the preselected period of time, the algae are killed by opening the large stopcock at the bottom of the flask, allowing the algal suspension to fall into alcohol in order to stop the reaction and extract the photosynthesized material. Although a variety of killing and extracting procedures have been tested, most of the experiments were performed by dropping the algae into alcohol so as to result in an 80% alcohol solution. The total amount of carbon fixed is then determined by taking an aliquot of this entire suspension, evaporating it to dryness on an aluminum disk and counting it on a GEIGER counter[1]. The fraction soluble is determined by either filtering or centrifuging the suspension and then recounting the clear supernate or filtrate.

The distribution of the fixed radiocarbon among the various compounds must now be determined. Since in

[1] M. CALVIN, C. HEIDELBERGER, J. C. REID, B. M. TOLBERT, and P. E. YANKWICH, *Isotopic Carbon* (John Wiley & Sons, Inc., New York, 1949).

relatively short periods of time most of the fixed radio-activity is found in the soluble components, the problem is one of analyzing for the distribution in the soluble fraction. This has been done by an application of the method of paper chromatography introduced and developed for amino acid analysis by Consden, Martin, and Synge[1]. It has since been applied to a wide variety of compounds and no detailed description of it will be given here. The unique extension to our work lies in the ability to locate particularly those compounds which contain the radioactive carbon atoms on the paper by means of a radioautograph of the resulting paper chromatogram obtained by allowing an X-ray film to remain in contact with the paper for a suitable period of time. Those areas of the paper which are occupied by radioactive compounds will, of course, expose the X-ray film. Such a map of the disposition of the radioactive compounds contained in an extract is shown in Figure 5. The chemical nature of the compounds defined by the exposed areas can be inferred from the position occupied by a compound with respects to the origin of the chromatogram. More precise determination of the chemical character is assisted by chemistry performed on the material eluted from the spot defined by the radiogram and rechromatography. Final identification, however, is usually dependent on the co-chromatography of the unknown, or questioned, radioactive material eluted from the paper with an authentic specimen of the suspected compound and the demonstration of the complete identity of the carrier material as determined by some visible test on the paper with the pattern of radioactivity in the co-chromatogram. The amount of radioactivity incorporated in these compounds can be determined quite accurately by using the X-ray film as a means of defining that area of the paper containing the compound, thus permitting the particular spot to be cut out from the larger and eluted from the paper and mounted on a plate to be counted.

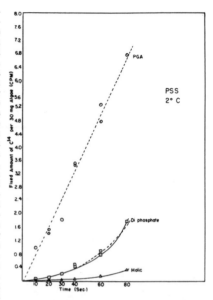

Fig. 6.—Behavior of radioactivity in specific compounds in extracts of *Scenedesmus*, exposed to radioactive carbon dioxide at 2°C.

A much simpler means would be to count the spot right on the paper with a Geiger counter. The fraction of the total amount of radioactivity in the spot which is thus registered by the Geiger counter is fairly constant for all compounds for any given chromatographic system. Thus, for most purposes it is sufficient simply to expose the paper to X-ray film in order to determine just where the radioactive spots are, and then having so defined them, to count them right on the paper for quantitative comparison, by the Geiger counter. It is clear from Figure 5 that the variety of products synthesized at room temperature by *Scenedesmus* (as well as by all other plants tried) is great, even in a very short time such as ten seconds. But even so, it is clear that the predominant compound as the time gets shorter is phosphoglyceric acid.

This is even more strongly demonstrated when the experiment is carried out at reduced temperature, for instance 2°C, so as to slow down all of the reactions and enable us to see more clearly the earliest products. Figure 6 shows a plot of the concentration of radioactivity per unit of algae for three of the major early compounds, formed at 2°C. On such a plot as this, it is clear that those substances which are formed directly from carbon dioxide with no appreciable intermediates

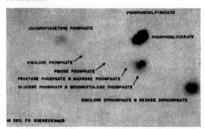

Fig. 5.—Radiogram of a paper chromatogram from 10 s $C^{14}O_2$ fixation in the light by *Scenedesmus*.

[1] R. Consden, A. H. Gordon, and A. J. P. Martin, Biochem. J. *38*, 224 (1944). – A. A. Benson, J. A. Bassham, M. Calvin, T. C. Goodale, V. A. Haas, and W. Stepka, J. Am. Chem. Soc. *72*, 1710 (1950).

Table I
C^{14} Distribution in Photosynthetic Products of Barley and *Scenedesmus*

Conditions[1]	Glyceric Acid			Glycolic Acid		Hexose		
	—COOH	—CHOH	—CH$_2$OH	—COOH	—CH$_2$OH	C 3,4	C 2,5	C 1,6
Barley								
Preillum:								
2 min dark . . .	96	2·6	1·7					
4 s PS	87	6·5	6·8	48·5	51·5			
15 s PS	56	21	23	50 ± 5	50 ± 5			
15 s PS	49	25	26					
30 s PS[2]				48	52	52	25	24
30 s PS[2]	75	6	9					
40 s PS				47	53			
60 s PS	44[3]	30	25					
Scenedesmus								
5 s PS	95[4]	2·5	1·2					
30 s PS						87[5]	7	6
30 s PS[6]MI[7] . . .	73	12	15					
60 s PS[6]	51	24	25					
60 s PS[6]MI	48	24	28					
60 s PS[6]								
60 s PS[6]MI	43	27	30					

[1] Experiments are steady-state photosynthesis, 10,000 footcandles unless otherwise stated. [2] 1000 footcandles. [3] Alanine obtained from this extract was 48% carboxyl-labeled. [4] Under the same conditions, *Chlorella* produced phosphoglycerate labeled 93%, 3% and 2%, respectively. [5] In this extract, malic acid was labeled 6·5% and aspartic acid 4% in the non-carboxyl carbons. [6] 3000 footcandles. [7] Malonate inhibited.

lying between them and carbon dioxide will be the only ones that will show a finite slope; all others should start with a zero slope. A finite slope is the case for phosphoglyceric acid and possibly for malic acid, indicating at least two independent carbon dioxide fixing reactions, one leading to a three-carbon compound and the other producing a four-carbon compound[1].

Since the hexose phosphates appear extremely early in all of these photosynthesis experiments and because of the known close relationship between the hexose phosphates and phosphoglyceric acids in the glycolytic sequence, it seemed most reasonable to suppose that these hexose phosphates were formed from the phosphoglyceric acid by a combination of the two three-carbon fragments derived from phosphoglyceric acid in an overall process very similar to, if not identical with, the reversal of glycolysis.

One means of testing this suggestion would be a comparison of the distribution of radioactivity in the three carbon atoms of glyceric acid with those in the hexose as shown in Table I. It thus appears that the hexose is indeed formed by the combination of two three-carbon molecules derived from the glyceric acid in such a manner that carbon atoms three and four of the hexose correspond to the carboxyl-carbon of the glyceric acid; carbon atoms two and five with the alpha-carbon; and carbon atoms one and six with the beta-carbon of the

glyceric acid. This correspondence is maintained when the distribution in these two compounds (glyceric acid and hexose) is compared for a wide variety of different times.

With this clear cut indication of the similarity between the path of hexose synthesis and the known path of its breakdown, another means of testing how closely this parallelism might be followed suggests itself. The hexose derivative which is last in the sequence of changes prior to the breakdown of the carbon skeleton during glycolysis is the fructose-1,6-diphosphate. Correspondingly, then, it presumably would be the first hexose derivative to appear in the reverse direction. If this is the case and, furthermore, if the hexose derivative reservoirs involved in sucrose synthesis are more or less isolated from those involved in storage and glycolysis, the radioactivity should appear in the fructose half of the sucrose molecule prior to its appearance in the glucose half. This is indeed the case[1]. However, sucrose does not seem to be formed by the simple reversal of the sucrose phosphorylase system which was described for certain bacteria[2], since for this to be the case, free fructose would have to be apparent in the photosynthesizing organism, whereas it is never so found, nor has the enzyme itself ever been isolated from any green plant.

[1] E. J. BADIN and M. CALVIN, J. Am. Chem. Soc. *72*, 5266 (1950). - S. KAWAGUCHI, A. A. BENSON, M. CALVIN, and P. M. HAYES, J. Am. Chem. Soc. *74*, 4477 (1952).

[1] S. KAWAGUCHI, A. A. BENSON, N. CALVIN, and P. M. HAYES, J. Am. Chem. Soc. *74*, 4477 (1952).
[2] W. Z. HASSID, M. DOUDOROFF, and H. A. BARKER, J. Am. Chem. Soc. *66*, 1416 (1944). - M. DOUDOROFF, H. A. BARKER, and W. Z. HASSID, J. Biol. Chem. *168*, 725 (1947).

83

The recent identification[1] as uridine diphosphoglucose (U.D.P.G.) of the spot which had been previously[2] called «the unknown glucose phosphate spot» has lead to another suggestion as to the mode of formation of sucrose. Glucose-labeled U.D.P.G. appears very early in the sequence of compounds formed. Furthermore, it has been possible to demonstrate the presence in the hexose monophosphate area of a sucrose phosphate by using a carefully selected phosphatase, containing no invertase, in the treatment of this entire phosphate area[3]. We have suggested, therefore, that U.D.P.G. may be involved in sucrose synthesis in a manner similar to that of glucose-1-phosphate in the numerous phosphorylase reactions, with the difference, however, that the acceptor of the glucose moiety would be some phosphate of fructose, thus producing a sucrose phosphate. Recent work by Putnam and Hassid[4] gives further support to the idea that only phosphorylated derivatives of glucose and fructose are involved in sucrose synthesis in higher plants. They found that in sucrose synthesis, from labeled glucose in leaf punches, no free fructose was formed, although the sucrose becomes equally labeled in both the glucose and fructose portions. Conversely, when labeled fructose is used, no free labeled glucose appears, while the sucrose is uniformly labeled in both moieties.

It is possible that compounds of the U.D.P.G. type could be concerned in the transformation of sugars and the subsequent incorporation into polysaccharides. Uridine diphosphate would thus serve as a carbon carrier in the same way that pyridine nucleotides and flavonucleotides are involved in hydrogen transfer; the adenylic acid system in phosphate transfer; and coenzyme A in the transfer of acetyl groups. There is already some evidence for the existence of other members of the uridine diphosphate group from our own work, as well as that of others[5].

We may now turn our attention from the fate of the glyceric acid to the problem of its origin. An examination of Table I indicates quite clearly that the first position in the glyceric acid to become labeled is the carboxyl group. As time proceeds, the other two carbon atoms in the glyceric acid acquire radioactivity and it

appears that they acquire it at equal rates, at least within the present accuracy of the experiments.

It thus appears that the most rapid reaction which carbon dioxide can undergo at least at high light intensities, is a condensation with a C_2 fragment leading directly to phosphoglyceric acid. An examination of the chromatograms of a very short photosynthetic period shows glycine and glycolic acid as the only two-carbon compounds present. The distribution of radioactivity among the carbon atoms of these two compounds is always equal and the same and corresponds very well with that in the alpha- and beta-carbon atoms of the glyceric acid, as may be seen from Table I. This suggests that glycolic acid either is in the direct line for the formation of the C_2 carbon dioxide acceptor, or is very closely related thereto.

The question now arises as to the source of this C_2 carbon dioxide acceptor. There are, of course, only two possibilities for its origin. Either it results from a one-plus-one combination or it must result from the splitting of a four-carbon compound or a larger one. In order for it to result from the combination of two one-carbon fragments there must exist as an intermediate some one-carbon compound more reduced than carbon dioxide which, in turn, may combine either with itself or with carbon dioxide. Furthermore, the reservoir of this one-carbon intermediate would have to be vanishingly small since all attempts to find labeled, reduced, one-carbon compounds, such as formic acid or formaldehyde, in the early stages of photosynthesis have failed and, in addition, the resulting two-carbon fragment is very nearly equally labeled in both carbon atoms.

One would also expect that these one-carbon compounds would tend to disappear under conditions of low carbon dioxide concentrations leading to the disappearance of the two-carbon condensation product resulting from them. This leads us to the supposition that the formation of glycolic acid would be expected to drop off under conditions of low carbon dioxide concentration which is the reverse of what is observed.

We are thus left with the following possibility for the C_2 compound—the cleavage of some C_4 or larger structure. The fact of the early appearance of label in malic acid, taken together with the lack of any appreciable amounts of label in the compounds of the tricarboxylic acid cycle[1], led us to the supposition that malic acid was either a precursor to, or very closely related to, a four-carbon compound which could be split to produce the required two-carbon fragment.

In the course of the search for the two-carbon acceptor, and its immediate precursors, two new compounds were identified as early products of carbon dioxide incorporation which seem to have little to do with the direct synthesis of hexoses and, therefore, had a very likely function in the regeneration of the two-

[1] J. G. Buchanan et al., in press. – J. G. Buchanan, J. A. Bassham, A. A. Benson, D. F. Bradley, M. Calvin, L. L. Daus, M. Goodman, P. M. Hayes, V. H. Lynch, L. T. Norris, and A. T. Wilson, *Phosphorus Metabolism*, Vol. II (Johns Hopkins Press, Baltimore, Maryland, 1952), in press.

[2] S. Kawaguchi, A. A. Benson, N. Calvin, and P. M. Hayes, J. Am. Chem. Soc. 74, 4477 (1952).

[3] J. G. Buchanan, J. A. Bassham, A. A. Benson, D. F. Bradley, M. Calvin, L. L. Daus, M. Goodman, P. M. Hayes, V. H. Lynch, L. T. Norris, and A. T. Wilson, *Phosphorus Metabolism*, Vol. II (Johns Hopkins Press, Baltimore, Maryland, 1952), in press. – J. G. Buchanan, in press.

[4] E. W. Putnam, Thesis (University of California, Berkeley, 1952).

[5] R. Caputto, L. F. Leloir, C. E. Cardini, and A. C. Paladini. J. Biol. Chem. 184, 333 (1950). – A. C. Paladini and L. F. Leloir, Biochem. J. 51, 426 (1951). – J. T. Park, J. Biol. Chem. 194, 885 (1952).

[1] A. A. Benson and M. Calvin, J. Exptl. Botany 1, 63 (1950).

carbon acceptor. These were the phosphates of the seven carbon sugar sedoheptulose and of the five carbon sugars ribulose, ribose and arabinose[1].

The question immediately presents itself as to the relation between these two compounds along the path of carbon assimilation, not only with each other but with the precursors which are already known and the possible products that might be formed from them. The attempt to answer this question focuses our attention once again upon some of the shortcomings and limitations of the method of observation that we are using and the nature of the experiment which we are performing. Our initial hope of determining the sequence of intermediates by a simple observation of a sequence of compounds into which radioactivity has been incorporated in steady state experiments is now complicated by the uncertainty as to the amount of compound present during the steady state. It is easy to visualize a situation in which the actual amount of intermediate present during the steady state is so small as to escape observation by our methods, or perhaps even to be so unstable as to be lost by our methods of observation. This complete failure of a compound to appear on a chromatogram, although it might conceivably be an intermediate, is, of course, an extreme case. The more usual situation is one in which most of the intermediates are present but in varying concentrations in the steady state. Under such conditions a single or even several observations of the relative amount of radioactivity incorporated into a variety of compounds would not necessarily be any real criterion of the relative order of these compounds in the sequence of events.

In order to achieve the full value of the method of observation then, it becomes necessary to perform rather extended kinetic experiments in which the appearance of radioactivity in all compounds is plotted as a function of time at sufficiently short intervals to enable a rather accurate and detailed curve to be obtained. Furthermore, the distribution of radioactivity among the atoms within each compound should also be determined as a function of time. The validity of any proposed sequence of events could then be determined by a comparison of the calculated appearance and distribution curves with those actually observed. In order to calculate such appearance curves, as well as the distribution curves amongst the atoms in each compound, one can set up a system of linear differential equations based upon the following model:

$$CO_2 \xrightarrow{R} A \xrightarrow{R} B \xrightarrow{R} - \to S \qquad (1)$$

where CO_2 represents the entering carbon dioxide; A, B, etc. represent intermediates involved in carbon

dioxide assimilation; S represents more or less final storage product; R is a measure of the total rate of carbon dioxide assimilation in the steady state expressed in moles of carbon per minute.

The rate of change of the specific activity of a single carbon atom in A, given by X_A, is then expressed by Equation (2). (The specific activity of the entering carbon dioxide is here taken as unity. $[A]$, the concentration of the compound A, is independent of time.)

$$\frac{dX_A}{dt} = \frac{R}{[A]} (1 - X_A). \qquad (2)$$

The specific activity of the corresponding atom in compound B is given by an exactly similar Equation (3).

$$\frac{dX_B}{dt} = \frac{R}{[B]} (X_A - X_B). \qquad (3)$$

Equations of identical form may be written for every atom of every compound that might be considered an intermediate. These equations may be solved explicitly by means of a differential analyzer provided two parameters are known. These are the total rate of entry of carbon into the system during the steady state, R, and the steady state concentration of each atom which might be considered as lying along the path of carbon assimilation $[A]$, $[B]$, etc.

It is clear that if such compounds (whose prime function it is to serve as carbon carriers between the entering carbon dioxide and the final storage products in the plant) do indeed exist in biological systems they would very soon become saturated with radioactivity. By this is meant that the amount of radioactivity observed in that particular compound would very soon reach a maximum value and remain that way. The reason for this is that by definition the amount of these intermediate compounds is not changing, and also is small compared to the total amount of carbon the plant assimilates during the experiment. Since all of the carbon, or at least most of it, must pass through these reservoirs of intermediates they will very soon acquire the same specific activity as the entering carbon dioxide. In contrast to this, those materials which are not functioning as simple intermediates but rather are functioning as storage reservoirs, or are very distant from the immediate photosynthetic intermediates, will not acquire radioactivity as rapidly, or if they do they will not become saturated as rapidly as those which are directly involved in the path of carbon assimilation. The amount of radioactivity found in those compounds which saturate in a relatively short time now provides a relatively easy method of determining the size of the functioning reservoirs of these compounds which are directly engaged in the path of carbon assimilation. A simple measurement of this amount compared to the specific activity of the entering carbon dioxide will provide a measure, in moles per unit volume of the

[1] A. A. BENSON, J. A. BASSHAM, M. CALVIN, A. G. HALL, H. E. HIRSCH, S. KAWAGUCHI, V. H. LYNCH, and N. E. TOLBERT, J. Biol. Chem. 196, 703 (1952).

biological material, of the compound in question. Furthermore, having once achieved a relatively uniform label in these photosynthetic intermediates, it becomes possible to follow the behavior of the reservoir size as a function of change in external variables, for example, light intensity. We have chosen to include in this review a more or less detailed description of just this determination of the effect of light intensity upon reservoir sizes as a means of describing the general experimental technique which is involved.

Steady state and reservoir sizes — Methods and results

The apparatus used for these experiments was constructed to permit the algal suspension to be left under controlled external conditions (illumination intensity, temperature, carbon dioxide and oxygen concentration) while photosynthesizing for at least one hour. Furthermore, it was required that the change, natural to radioactive carbon dioxide, which was to be circulated in a closed system, and the withdrawal of several samples at given time intervals be accomplished with a minimum of change in these conditions.

The apparatus consisted of:

(a) A square illumination vessel A (Fig. 7) made out of Lucite (polyacrylic plastic), 49 cm high, 11 cm wide and 0·7 cm thick (inside dimensions). The bottom was provided with a gas inlet tube with five small holes to allow good contact between gas and liquid and a drain tube closed with a screw clamp. The top of the vessel was provided with a gas outlet tube. A water-alcohol mixture from a constant temperature bath was allowed to flow over the outer surfaces of the vessel in order to control the temperature of the suspension.

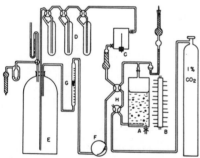

Fig. 7.—Diagram of the assembly for steady state photosynthesis. (For explanation of the letters, see text.)

(b) Two illumination banks (represented by B), each with four fluorescent tubes (General Electric, quality white, 20 W each), providing an almost uniform illumination over the whole surface of the vessel, of 7×10^4 ergs./cm^2 (roughly 700 footcandles).

Fig. 8.—Assembly for steady state photosynthesis. (For explanation of the letters, see text.)

(c) An ionization chamber C, connected to a recording vibrating reed electrometer, to record the activity of the gas leaving the vessel continually during the run.

(d) Three gas traps D, to permit the addition of a known amount of radioactive carbon dioxide to the system, and trap the remaining radioactivity after the run.

(e) A flask E, of 5 l volume, containing a mixture of 1% radioactive carbon dioxide in air. The reservoir contained so much carbon dioxide that the algae assimilated no more than 20% of it during a run.

(f) A gas circulating pump F of the rubber tubing type, and a flow meter G.

(g) A system of four-way stopcocks H, which permitted the vessel to be flushed with a mixture of 1% ordinary carbon dioxide in air, from the cylinder I. The assembly is shown in Figure 8.

In a typical experiment, 2 cm^3 (wet packed) of one-day old *Scenedesmus*, washed and resuspended in 200 cm^3 of deionized water, were placed in the vessel and aerated with the ordinary gas mixture for at least one-half hour, while the mixture of radioactive carbon dioxide circulated in the gas system for thorough mixing, without passing through the vessel. The suspension was kept at 24 °C. After this time, during which a steady state of photosynthesis had been reached, the radioactive mixture was passed through the vessel in place of the ordinary gas mixture, by a manipulation

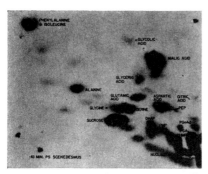

Fig. 9.—Radiogram of a paper chromatogram from 10 min. $C^{14}O_2$ fixation in light by *Scenedesmus*. 1% suspension, 1% CO_2 in air; light intensity 7×10^4 ergs./cm^2-s. D.H.A.P.: dihydroxyacetone phosphate; P.E.B.:phosphoenolpyruvic acid; P.M.P.:pentose monophosphates; P.Go.A.:phosphoglycolic acid; P.G.A.:phosphoglyceric acid; H.M.P.: hexose monophosphates; D.P.:pentose and hexose diphosphates.

of the pair of stopcocks at H, and samples of 20 cm^3 of the suspension withdrawn at intervals of five or ten minutes. These samples were dropped into 80 cm^3 of alcohol of room temperature, to make an extraction in 80% alcohol. After 30 min of photosynthesis, the

lights were turned off and the suspension allowed to remain in the dark for a period of 5 min, during which time again several samples were withdrawn, and treated in the same manner. In one experiment another light period followed the dark period.

The samples were shaken for 1 h and centrifuged. The residue was re-extracted in 50 cm^3 of 20% alcohol at room temperature, centrifuged, and re-extracted again with 20 cm^3 of water. The extracts were concentrated together to 0·5 cm^3.

An aliquot of the concentrate equivalent to 30 μl of packed cells was evaporated on a corner of a filter paper (WHATMAN #1), and the chromatogram run with water-saturated phenol in one direction and n-butanol-propionic acid-water in the other. The chromatograms were exposed to X-ray film for about two weeks[1]. The labeled compounds appeared on it as black spots. Figure 9 shows the radiogram for ten minute photosynthesis of *Scenedesmus*. The amount of radioactivity contained in the different compounds was determined by counting the corresponding spots on the paper directly with a large-area GEIGER-MÜLLER tube with thin mica window. The compounds were identified by a combination of the following criteria: (a) Their position on the paper; (b) the spot was cut out, eluted from the paper with water and run again in suitable solvents, together with such an amount of the suspected com-

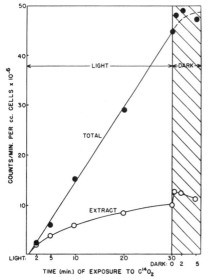

Fig. 10. —$C^{14}O_2$ fixation by *Scenedesmus*. 1% suspension, 1% CO_2 in air, light intensity 7×10^4 ergs./cm^2-s.

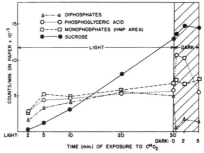

Fig. 11.—Behavior of radioactivity in specific compounds in the extract from the experiment of Figure 10.

pound that it could be detected by a specific spraying reagent. The black spot on the film had to coincide accurately with the color reaction; (c) the eluted spot was chemically transformed (e.g. treating the sugar phosphates with phosphatase) and the resulting compound cochromatographed with carrier detectable by spray.

Figure 10 shows the total and the extracted amounts of radiocarbon fixed by 1 cm^3 cells during 30 min of

[1] M. CALVIN. J. Chem. Education 26, 639 (1949).

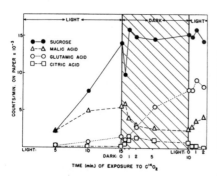

Fig. 12.—Behavior of radioactivity in specific compounds in the extract from an experiment done under conditions corresponding to those of Figure 10.

photosynthesis followed by 5 min of darkness. The slope in the total fixation curve in the light corresponds to a 13 cm³ CO_2 assimilation (N.T.P.) per hour.

Figure 11 shows the amount of radioactivity incorporated into sucrose and three phosphorus compounds for the experiment of Figure 10.

Figure 12 gives the number of counts in sucrose, glutamic, malic and citric acid, for a different experiment of 15 min photosynthesis, followed by 10 min dark, and again 5 min of photosynthesis.

Although the variation between experiments is quite high, there are some striking features which are common to all:

(1) The curves of some of the compounds show a marked decrease in slope after 5 min of photosynthesis. This quite clearly indicates the presence of rapidly turning-over reservoirs in the photosynthesis cycle which are then thoroughly labeled and reach the specific activity of the fed carbon dioxide: Diphosphate area (mainly ribulose diphosphate); hexose-monophosphate area (50% glucose-, 26% sedoheptulose-, some fructose- and mannose-monophosphate); phosphoglyceric acid. The leveling off of these curves permits the calculation of the concentration of the reservoirs of those compounds in the photosynthesis cycle, by dividing the measured amount of radioactivity per carbon atom by the specific activity of the fed carbon dioxide[1].

Table II gives the steady state concentrations during photosynthesis for some compounds determined by this method.

(2) The fact that the activity vs. time curves show a definite yet low slope for as long as 30 min can be taken to indicate that the breakdown of carbohydrates

[1] The efficiency factor of the counting of spots on papers has been determined by converting three cut out spots to barium carbonate and measuring their activity in an ionization chamber. It is 19 disintegrations per count.

Table II

Steady State Concentrations of Some Compounds Involved in the Photosynthesis Cycle. *Scenedesmus*, experimental conditions as in Figure 10

Substance	μmoles/cm³ cells[1]
Phosphoglyceric acid	1·4
Dihydroxyacetone phosphate . .	0·17
Fructose phosphate	0·12
Glucose phosphate	0·4
Mannose phosphate	0·05
Sedoheptulose phosphate	0·18
Ribulose diphosphate	0·5
Alanine	0·2

continues throughout the illumination, i.e. their formation from photosynthetic intermediates is reversible. Thus, there are two sources of the intermediates: (a) the carbon dioxide fed; the amount of compound formed from this source reaches the maximum specific activity in 5 to 10 min; (b) the carbohydrate pool of the cells; the amount formed from this source is labeled only slowly since the specific activity of the carbohydrate pool rises slowly due to the large size of the pool.

(3) Other compounds show almost constant rate of labeling during the whole period of photosynthesis; sucrose, malic and glutamic acid. For this and other reasons it is clear that these compounds are not in the photosynthesis cycle, but are formed during the photosynthesis at a constant rate. Their large reservoirs in the cells are labeled only slowly.

Table III

Phosphatase Treatment of H.M.P. Area after 30 min Photosynthesis and 30 min Photosynthesis Followed by 5 min Dark

Substance	Number of counts/min on paper	
	30 min P.S.	30 min P.S. 5 min D.
Glucose	3140	4280
Fructose	910	1040
Sedoheptulose	1600	} 1210[2]
Mannose	460	

(4) When illumination is interrupted there appears a sudden great increase in the concentration of phosphoglyceric acid (followed by a slow decrease after 2 min), and an almost complete depletion of the diphosphate area. Analysis of the monophosphate area showed that the amount of sedoheptulose phosphate decreased also (cf. Table III). The concentration of

[1] Volume measured as wet packed cells

[2] An appreciable fraction of this count is certainly hexose so that one may estimate a maximum value of the heptose at around 800 counts/min.

malic acid decreases as well. The rate of labeling of glutamic acid is increased greatly after a short induction period; citric acid, which contains little activity during the whole light period, shows a sudden increase in the dark, followed by a slow decrease. The labeling of sucrose continues at the same rate as in light for about 1 min, after which it is stopped almost completely.

Both experiments gave the same picture for most of the compounds, with the two exceptions: In the second experiment the diphosphate area, which in the first contained almost the same number of counts as phosphoglyceric acid during the light, had only about 15% of it in this second run. This value dropped to 5% in the dark. The phosphoglyceric acid showed a hardly significant rise in the dark during the first 2 min, but again a slow decrease after 5 min. Although we do not know why in this experiment the concentration of ribulose diphosphate was so low in the light, the coincidence with the lack of increase of phosphoglyceric acid points to a connection between both effects.

(5) In the light following the dark, the diphosphates, phosphoglyceric and malic acid increase again.

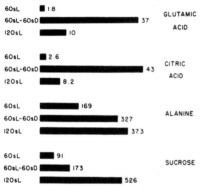

60sL	▮ 1.8	GLUTAMIC
60sL-60sD	████████████████ 37	ACID
120sL	█████ 10	

60sL	▮ 2.6	CITRIC
60sL-60sD	██████████████████ 43	ACID
120sL	█████ 8.2	

60sL	████████ 169	ALANINE
60sL-60sD	███████████████ 327	
120sL	████████████████ 373	

60sL	█████ 91	SUCROSE
60sL-60sD	████████ 173	
120sL	████████████████ 526	

Fig. 13.—Effect of light and dark on the labeling of glutamic and citric acid. 0·1% suspension, light intensity $1\cdot6 \times 10^5$ ergs/cm²·s (Numbers: counts/min x 10^{-3} on paper per cm³ cells).

The effect of dark on the labeling of glutamic and citric acid was already reported in an earlier paper[1] and studied more closely in the following experiments: 0·2 cm³ wet packed algae (*Chlorella pyrenoidosa*) were suspended in 200 cm³ distilled water, illuminated in a flat circular vessel of 1 cm thickness by incandescent lights through an infra red filter (intensity $1\cdot6 \times 10^5$ergs/ cm²·s) and aerated with 0·08% carbon dioxide in air. The low concentration of cells was chosen to avoid shading of cells in the suspension, so that during the light period all the cells were illuminated continually.

[1] M. Calvin, J. Chem. Education *26*, 639 (1949).

After one-half hour, the aeration bubbler was taken out and a suitable amount of radioactive bicarbonate (sodium) solution added. (The algae, which were grown in slightly acid medium, had enough buffering capacity to convert the bicarbonate to carbon dioxide). The vessel was immediately stoppered and shaken in the light. After 1 min, the suspension was drained into

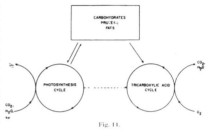

Fig. 14.

a darkened flask, and after another minute poured into four times its volume of boiling alcohol. Control samples were treated in the same way, but kept in the light, in contact with radioactive carbon dioxide for 1 and 2 min, respectively. The analysis of the fixed radioactivity was performed by paper chromatography and radioautography with the technique already described. The results are shown in Figure 13.

Discussion

It has already been pointed out that photosynthesis is not a mere reversal of respiration; this was supported by the observation that the carbon of newly formed photosynthetic intermediates is not available for respiration while the light is on[1]. We may thus represent the relationship between photosynthesis and respiration by the following scheme (See Figure 14). The labeling of the Krebs cycle intermediates through the storage products (carbohydrates, fats, proteins) of the cells is a slow process, due to the relatively large size of the storage pools. The fact that the photosynthesis intermediates find their way into the tricarboxylic acid cycle very rapidly after the light is switched off means that there is another connection between the two cycles which is blocked as long as the light is on but becomes accessible in the dark. This was interpreted in earlier work[2] in terms of the action of the light in maintaining at low concentration the intermediate required for entry into the tricarboxylic acid cycle. A closer specification of how this is accomplished is now possible since the discovery that alpha-lipoic acid is a

[1] M. Calvin, J. Chem. Education *26*, 639 (1949). – J. W. Weigl, P. M. Warrington, and M. Calvin, J. Am. Chem. Soc. *73*, 5058 (1951).

[2] M. Calvin, J. Chem. Education *26*, 639 (1949).

cofactor for the oxidative decarboxylation of pyruvic acid to an active acetyl group[1] which is the one reaction known to feed the KREBS cycle[2]. The mechanism of the reaction may be written this way:

$$CH_3\;HC-CH_2-CH_2-CH_2-CO-Thiamin+CH_3-CO-COOH$$
(Co-pyruvate oxidase)   (Pyruvic acid)

          Coenzyme A

$$CH_2\;CH_2\;CH-R + Acetyl\;CoA + CO_2$$

The reduced lipoic acid complex would then be reoxidized to the disulfide form by a suitable oxidant (e.g. pyridine or flavin nucleotides). In order that the oxidation of pyruvic acid can proceed, the enzyme has to be present in its oxidized form. If it is kept in its reduced form under the influence of the light-produced reducing power, the reaction cannot proceed and the pyruvic acid formed during photosynthesis will not find its way into the respiratory cycle. The reaction is inhibited because only a small amount of the enzyme catalyzing it exists in the required form, most of it being kept in the other form under the "pressure" of the reducing power generated by the light energy. This recalls a similar phenomenon which has been known for a long time, i.e. the suppression of the fermentation of carbohydrates in favor of their oxidation under aerobic conditions (PASTEUR effect). This effect has been explained in a manner similar to the one used here to account for the inhibition of the respiration of photosynthetic intermediates[3]. The reduction of acetaldehyde to alcohol requires a dehydrogenase in its reduced form; under aerobic conditions the dehydrogenase exists primarily in its oxidized form, and the acetaldehyde instead of being reduced is oxidized to acetic acid.

The sudden rise in phosphoglyceric acid and the decrease in ribulose diphosphate and sedoheptulose

phosphate in the dark period, together with the observation that the dark rise in phosphoglyceric acid is absent when the ribulose diphosphate concentration was low during the light, confirms the earlier suggestion that the phosphates of the C_7 and C_5 sugars are precursors of the C_2 carbon dioxide acceptor[1]. This, together with evidence gathered in previous work[2] leads to the following scheme for the photosynthetic cycle[3] (Fig. 15).

Upon this basis an attempt might be made to relate the two effects as follows; when the light is turned off, the reduction reactions requiring light are stopped, whereas cleavage and carboxylation reactions continue until their substrates are exhausted. Presumably, this would lead to a depletion of the C_5 and C_7 sugars, the synthesis of which requires reduction steps (particularly the six-equivalents leading to the tetrose which itself is a very small reservoir), and a rise of phosphoglyceric acid, the further fate of which is also dependent upon reduction. However, a number of arguments seem to contradict this view: (1) The observation that plants fix radiocarbon in the dark immediately following a light period at low carbon dioxide concentration, to form a similar pattern of compounds as the one found in photosynthesis shows that the sequence following phosphoglyceric acid is not blocked at once upon cessation of illumination, but that the cells contain sufficient reducing power to transform some phosphoglyceric acid into carbohydrates; (2) the cleavage of the pentoses and heptoses into the C_2 carbon dioxide acceptor and a triose and pentose respectively is dependent on a reduction step as well.

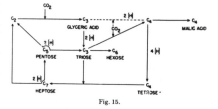

Fig. 15.

We are thus led to the suggestion that the rise in phosphoglyceric acid is not be explained by a mere interruption of the sequence, but that the rate of production of phosphoglyceric acid at some time in the

[1] L. J. REED, I. C. GUNSALUS, et al., J. Am. Chem. Soc. 73, 5920 (1951). – E. L. PATTERSON, et al., J. Am. Chem. Soc. 73, 5919 (1951). – I. C. GUNSALUS, L. STRUGLIA, and D. J. O'KANE, J. Biol. Chem. 194, 859 (1952). – L. J. REED and B. G. DE BUSK, J. Am. Chem. Soc. 74, 3457 (1952). – M. W. BULLOCK, et al., J. Am. Chem. Soc. 74, 3455 (1952).

[2] S. OCHOA, J. R. STERN, and M. C. SCHNEIDER, J. Biol. Chem. 193, 691 (1951). – S. KORKES, A. DEL CAMILLO, I. C. GUNSALUS, and S. OCHOA, J. Biol. Chem. 193, 721 (1951).

[3] O. MEYERHOF, Amer. Scientist 40, 483 (1952).

[1] A. A. BENSON, J. A. BASSHAM, M. CALVIN, A. G. HALL, H. E. HIRSCH, S. KAWAGUCHI, V. H. LYNCH, and N. E. TOLBERT, J. Biol. Chem. 196, 703 (1952).

[2] S. KAWAGUCHI, A. A. BENSON, M. CALVIN, and P. M. HAYES, J. Am. Chem. Soc. 74, 4477 (1952). – M. CALVIN, The Harvey Lectures 46, 213–251, 1951, in press.

[3] This scheme is intended to represent only changes in the carbon skeletons. The reducing equivalents are indicated only to show redox relationships between the known compounds. A number of the isolated compounds are isoximers and have not been included.

$$HO_3P-OCH_2-CHOH-CHOH-CO-CH_2-O-PO_3H$$

$$\xrightarrow{CO_2,\ 2[H]}
\begin{cases}
HO_3P-OCH_2-CHOH-CHO \\
\text{phosphoglyceraldehyde} \\
{}^-HO_3P-OCH_2-CHOH-COOH \\
\text{phosphoglyceric acid}
\end{cases}$$

$$\xrightarrow[\text{dark}]{CO_2} \quad 2x{}^-HO_3P-OCH_2-CHOH-COOH$$
$$\text{phosphoglyceric acid}$$

first minute of darkness is actually higher than it is in the steady state photosynthesis. This would be the case if the C_3–C_2 cleavage of ribulose diphosphate, which in photosynthesis presumably yields a triose phosphate molecule beside the C_2 carbon dioxide acceptor, in the dark yields a molecule of phosphoglyceric acid instead of the triose molecule. The overall reactions may be represented above (not a mechanism).

This hypothesis is supported by the fact that the triose phosphate also decreases in the dark.

The fact that the net result of the reaction sequence in the light from ribulose diphosphate to phosphoglyceric acid and triose phosphate is a reductive carboxylation and thus the reversal of the oxidative decarboxylation which, in the case of pyruvic acid, requires the presence of a cyclic disulfide compound leads to the idea that the former sequence might be catalyzed by a similar enzyme. This idea seems to be supported by the results of an experiment performed in this laboratory some time ago, which were difficult to explain[1].

In order to examine the relation between photosynthesis and the glycolytic cycle, a series of experiments similar to those described previously were performed with added iodoacetamide which is known to inhibit the action of triose phosphate dehydrogenase[2], presumably through a reaction with its sulfhydryl group[3]. A 1% suspension of Chlorella in phosphate buffer was allowed to photosynthesize in light of 2500 footcandles and an atmosphere of 1% carbon dioxide, 5% oxygen and 94% nitrogen. At various times before adding the radioactive bicarbonate solution, iodoacetamide was added to give a 1.5×10^{-4} M solution. 1 min after adding the radiocarbon, the cells were killed and extracted.

After 8 min contact with iodoacetamide, the cells were still able to fix 75% as much carbon dioxide as non-poisoned cells otherwise treated the same way (control). The amount of radioactivity in phosphoglyceric acid was 50% of the control, and the amount in sucrose had reached a sharp maximum of 3·5 times

that in the control. There was practically no radioactivity in the ribulose diphosphate. After 90 min of exposure to the poison the cells had practically lost their ability of photosynthesis.

If, in the proposed photosynthetic cycle, the cleavage of the heptose and pentose phosphates is dependent on an enzyme containing sulfhydryl groups, which were more sensitive to iodoacetamide than the triose phosphate dehydrogenase, a picture similar to the one described would be expected: After short exposure to the poison, in relatively low concentration, the lack of C_2 carbon dioxide acceptor would slow down the photosynthetic cycle. The synthesis of carbohydrates, however, would proceed almost without inhibition, thus decreasing the concentrations of the intermediates in the cycle. This would allow the compounds to reach a higher specific activity during the period of exposure to radiocarbon (cf. equation (2), change of specific activity inversly proportional to concentration]. At some time after administration of the poison, the sucrose would be labeled faster than in the control due to the higher specific activity of its precursors. After a longer period, however, the rate of synthesis of sucrose would decrease because the pool of its precursors would be exhausted.

Zusammenfassung

Die Trennung des Phänomens der Photosynthese grüner Pflanzen in eine Lichtreaktion und die vom Licht unabhängige Reduktion der Kohlensäure werden diskutiert.

Die Reduktion der Kohlensäure und das Schicksal des assimilierten Kohlenstoffs wurden untersucht mit Hilfe der Spurenmethode (Markierung der assimilierten Kohlensäure mit C[14]) und der Papierchromatographie. Ein Reaktionszyklus wird vorgeschlagen, in dem Phosphoglyzerinsäure das erste isolierbare Assimilationsprodukt ist.

Analysierung des Extraktes von Algen, die in einem stationären Zustand für längere Zeit radioaktive Kohlensäure assimilierten, lieferte weitere Auskunft über den vorgeschlagenen Zyklus und gestattete, die am Zyklus beteiligten Mengen einiger Substanzen ungefähr zu bestimmen. Die frühere Vermutung, dass Licht den Respirationszyklus beeinflusst, wird bestätigt. Die Möglichkeit der Mitwirkung von α-Liponsäure (α-lipoic acid) oder einer verwandten Substanz, bei diesem Effekt und im Photosynthesezyklus, wird erörtert.

[1] W. Stepka, Thesis University of California (June 1951).
[2] O. Meyerhof and W. Kiessling, Biochem. Z. 281, 249 (1953).
[3] L. Rapkins, C. r. Soc. Biol. (Paris) 112, 1294 (1933).

[Contribution from Radiation Laboratory and Department of Chemistry, University of California, Berkeley]

The Path of Carbon in Photosynthesis. XXI. The Cyclic Regeneration of Carbon Dioxide Acceptor[1]

By J. A. Bassham, A. A. Benson, Lorel D. Kay, Anne Z. Harris, A. T. Wilson and M. Calvin

Received October 16, 1953

Photosynthesizing plants have been exposed to $C^{14}O_2$ for short periods of time (0.4 to 15 sec.) and the products of carbon dioxide reduction analyzed by paper chromatography and radioautography. Methods have been developed for the degradation of ribulose and sedoheptulose. These sugars, obtained as their phosphate esters from the above $C^{14}O_2$ exposures and from other experiments, have been degraded and their distribution of radiocarbon determined. The distribution of radiocarbon in these sugars, and other data, indicate that sedoheptulose phosphate and ribulose diphosphates are formed during photosynthesis from triose and hexose phosphates, the latter being synthesized, in turn, by the reduction of 3-phosphoglyceric acid. Further evidence has been found for the previously proposed carboxylation of ribulose diphosphate to phosphoglyceric acid. Free energy calculations indicate this step would proceed spontaneously if enzymatically catalyzed. The efficiency of this cycle for reduction of CO_2 to hexose would be 0.9 if the reduction of each molecule of PGA requires the concurrent conversion of one molecule of ATP and one of DPN (red) to ADP, inorganic phosphate and DPN (ox.).

Previously reported tracer studies of the path of carbon in photosynthesis[2] led to the conclusion that carbon is incorporated by a carboxylation re-

action leading to phosphoglyceric acid (PGA)[3] which is then reduced and condensed to fructose

(1) The work described in this paper was sponsored by the U. S. Atomic Energy Commission. This paper was presented before the Division of Biological Chemistry, American Chemical Society, at the 124th National Meeting, Chicago, Illinois, September, 1953.

(2) M. Calvin, "The Harvey Lectures," Charles C Thomas Publishing Company, Springfield, Ill., 1950–51, p. 218.

(3) The following abbreviations will be used throughout this paper: PGA, phosphoglyceric acid; DHAP, dihydroxyacetone phosphate; FMP, fructose monophosphate; GMP, glucose monophosphate; SMP, sedoheptulose monophosphate; RDP ribulose diphosphate; ADP, adenosine diphosphate. ATP adenosine triphosphate; DPN, diphosphopyridine nucleotide (Coenzyme I), oxidized form; DPN[H₂], diphosphopyridine nucleotide, reduced form.

and glucose phosphates by a series of reactions similar to a reversal of glycolysis. These conclusions were supported by the observations that when carbon-14 is administered to the photosynthesizing plant as $C^{14}O_2$, the first radioactive compound isolated is carboxyl-labeled PGA, followed shortly by dihydroxyacetone phosphate (DHAP), fructose monophosphates (FMP) and glucose monophosphate (GMP), both hexoses being 3,4-labeled. After longer exposures of the plant to $C^{14}O_2$, radiocarbon appears in other carbon atoms of PGA and hexose and the distribution of activity is in agreement with the above conclusions.

$$\begin{array}{ccccccc}
{}^{*}\text{C} & & {}^{*}\text{C} & & {}^{*}\text{C} & & {}^{*}\text{C} \\
| & & | & & | & & | \\
{}^{*}\text{C} + \text{C}^{**}\text{O}_2 \longrightarrow & {}^{*}\text{C} & \xrightarrow{2[H]} & {}^{*}\text{C} \longrightarrow & {}^{*}\text{C} \\
& {}^{**}\text{C} & & {}^{**}\text{C} & & {}^{**}\text{C} \\
& & & & & | \\
& & & & & {}^{**}\text{C} \\
& & & & & | \\
\text{A} & \text{PGA} & \text{triose} & & {}^{*}\text{C} \\
& & & & | \\
& & & & {}^{*}\text{C} \\
& & & & \text{hexose}
\end{array}$$

Observations on the rate and distribution of labeling of malic acid[4-6] showed it to be the eventual product of a second carboxylation reaction which is accelerated during photosynthesis, and it was proposed that this second carboxylation played a part in the reduction of carbon in photosynthesis, leading eventually to the formation of the two-carbon CO_2 acceptor (A, above). Malic acid, itself, apparently was precluded as an actual intermediate by inhibition studies,[7] but was thought to be an indicator of an unstable intermediate which was actually the first product of the second carboxylation. The discovery[8] of rapidly labeled sedoheptulose monophosphate (SMP) and ribulose diphosphate (RDP) led to their inclusion in the proposed carbon reduction cycle leading to the two-carbon CO_2 acceptor.

The reciprocal changes in reservoir sizes of RDP and PGA observed when algae were subjected to light and dark periods[9] indicated a close relationship, perhaps identity, between the RDP and the two-carbon CO_2 acceptor.

In order to test these conclusions, it was necessary to design experiments involving very short exposures of the plant to $C^{14}O_2$. In some of these experiments, the C^{14} was administered during "steady state" photosynthesis, the environmental conditions (light, carbon dioxide pressure, etc.) being kept as nearly constant as possible for the hour preceding and the time during the experiment. Degradation methods have been developed for sedoheptulose and ribulose and complete distribution of radioactivity within these sugars obtained.

The results of these experiments seem to obviate the possibility that the second carboxylation reac-

(4) A. A. Benson, S. Kawaguchi, P. M. Hayes and M. Calvin, This Journal, **74**, 4477 (1952).

(5) A. A. Benson, *et al.*, "Photosynthesis in Plants," Iowa State College Press, Ames, Iowa, 1949, p. 381.

(6) D. W. Racusen and S. Aronoff, *Arch. Biochem. Biophys.*, **42**, 25 (1953).

(7) J. A. Bassham, A. A. Benson and M. Calvin, *J. Biol. Chem.*, **185**, 781 (1950).

(8) A. A. Benson, *et al.*, *ibid.*, **196**, 703 (1952).

(9) M. Calvin and Peter Massini, *Experientia*, **8**, 445 (1952).

tion (leading to malic acid) is a step in carbon reduction during photosynthesis. Since no new evidence has been found for the second "photosynthetic" carboxylation, it would appear that a carbon reduction cycle involving only one carboxylation (leading to PGA) is more likely than the previously proposed two-carboxylation cycle.

Experimental Procedure

Short "Steady State" Experiments.—Algae (*Scenedesmus obliquus*) were grown under controlled conditions,[5] centrifuged from the growth medium, and resuspended in a 1% by volume suspension in distilled water This suspension was placed in a rectangular, water-jacketed illumination chamber 6 mm. thick, through which was passed a continuous stream of 4% CO_2-in-air (Fig. 1). From the bottom of the chamber, a transparent tube led to a small transparent pump constructed of appropriately placed glass valves and two 5-cc. glass syringes mounted on a lever arm in such a position that the syringe plungers moved in and out reciprocally about 5 mm. when the lever arm was moved back and forth by a motor-driven eccentric. The output of the pump was divided, the major portion being returned to the illumination chamber and a smaller portion (20 ml./minute) forced to flow through a length of transparent "Transflex" tubing of about 1 mm. diameter and thence into a beaker containing boiling methanol. This solvent was found to have an apparent killing time of less than 0.2 sec. as determined by the cessation of carbon fixation during photosynthesis. The linear flow rate of algal suspension in the tube was about 57 cm./second. A solution of $C^{14}O_2$ in water (0.0716 M, 110 $\mu c./ml.$) in a 30-cc. syringe was injected through a fine hypodermic needle into the Transflex tubing at a point a selected distance from the end of the tubing. From the known flow rate of algal suspension in the Transflex tubing and distance of flow from the point of injection of $C^{14}O_2$ to the killing solution, the time of exposure of the algae to C^{14} was calculated. The flow of the $C^{14}O_2$-containing solution was controlled by driving the syringe plunger with a constant speed motor, and the flow rate was 0.5 ml./ minute. The resultant dilution of the algal suspension was 2.5% and the increment in total CO_2 concentration less than 15%.

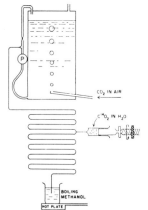

Fig. 1.—Schematic diagram of flow system for short exposure of algae to $C^{14}O_2$.

Since the flow of algal suspension in the tubing was not turbulent, some difference in rates of flow at the center and at the edge of the tubing was unavoidable. The extent of this difference was approximately determined by injecting a concentrated dye solution for about 0.5 sec. through the hypodermic needle while the flow rate in the tubing was 20

DEGRADATION OF SEDOHEPTULOSE

$$\begin{array}{c} \text{H} \\ \text{HC}=\text{N}-\text{N}-\text{C}_6\text{H}_5 \\ | \\ \text{C}=\text{N}-\text{N}-\text{C}_6\text{H}_5 \\ | \quad\quad \text{H} \\ \text{HOCH} \\ | \\ \text{HCOH} \\ | \\ \text{HCOH} \\ | \\ \text{HCOH} \\ | \\ \text{CH}_2\text{OH} \end{array} \xrightarrow[\text{NaHCO}_3]{\text{HIO}_4} \begin{array}{c} \text{H} \\ \text{HC}=\text{N}-\text{N}-\text{C}_6\text{H}_5 \\ | \\ \text{C}=\text{N}-\text{N}-\text{C}_6\text{H}_5 \\ | \quad \text{H} \\ \text{CHO} \\ \\ 1, 2, 3 \end{array} + 3\text{HCOOH} + \text{HCHO}$$

$$4, 5, 6 \quad\quad\quad 7$$

Phenyl-
hydrazine
HCl

$$\begin{array}{c} \text{CH}_2\text{OH} \\ | \\ \text{C}=\text{O} \\ | \\ \text{HOCH} \\ | \\ \text{HCOH} \\ | \\ \text{HCOH} \\ | \\ \text{HCOH} \\ | \\ \text{CH}_2\text{OH} \end{array} \xrightarrow[100°]{\text{Dowex-50}} \begin{array}{c} \text{CH}_2\text{OH} \\ | \\ \text{C} \\ | \\ \text{HOCH} \\ O \; | \; O \\ \text{HCOH} \\ | \\ \text{HCOH} \\ | \\ \text{CH} \\ | \\ \text{H}_2\text{C} \end{array} \xrightarrow{\text{NaIO}_4} \begin{array}{c} \text{HCOOH} \\ 4 \end{array} + \begin{array}{c} \text{CH}_2\text{OH} \\ | \\ \text{C} \\ | \\ O \; \text{CHO} \; O \\ \text{CHO} \\ | \\ \text{CH} \\ | \\ \text{H}_2\text{C} \end{array}$$

$$\xrightarrow[\text{Ce(ClO}_4)_6^-]{\text{H}^+} \begin{array}{c} \text{CO}_2 \\ 2 \end{array} + 6\text{HCOOH}$$

$$\downarrow \begin{array}{c} \text{H}_2 \\ \text{PtO}_2 \end{array}$$

$$\begin{array}{c} \text{CH}_2\text{OH} \\ | \\ \text{HCOH} \\ | \\ \text{HOCH} \\ | \\ \text{HCOH} \\ | \\ \text{HCOH} \\ | \\ \text{HCOH} \\ | \\ \text{CH}_2\text{OH} \end{array} + \begin{array}{c} \text{CH}_2\text{OH} \\ | \\ \text{HOCH} \\ | \\ \text{HOCH} \\ | \\ \text{HCOH} \\ | \\ \text{HCOH} \\ | \\ \text{HCOH} \\ | \\ \text{CH}_2\text{OH} \end{array} \xrightarrow{\text{HIO}_4} \begin{array}{c} 2\text{HCHO} \\ 1, 7 \end{array} + \begin{array}{c} 5\text{HCOOH} \\ 2, 3, 4, 5, 6 \end{array}$$

Acetobacter
suboxydans

Acetobacter
     suboxydans

$$\longrightarrow \text{Sedoheptulose} + \text{Mannoheptulose}$$

$$\begin{array}{c} \text{CH}_2\text{OH} \\ | \\ \text{HCOH} \\ | \\ \text{HOCH} \\ | \\ \text{HCOH} \\ | \\ \text{HCOH} \\ | \\ \text{C}=\text{O} \\ | \\ \text{CH}_2\text{OH} \end{array} \xrightarrow[\text{Ce(ClO}_4)_6^-]{\text{H}^+} \begin{array}{c} \text{CO}_2 \\ 6 \end{array} + 6\text{HCOOH}$$

Guloheptulose

ml./minute and observing the spreading of color during its travel through the tubing. For the longest length of tubing used, the dye was seen to reach the end of the tubing between 14 and 17 seconds, and at a shorter time between 9 and 11 seconds, so that the spread of flow in time appeared to be about 20% of the flow time. The times given are average times of exposure of the algae to C^{14}. Use of the dye also permitted observation of the mixing of C^{14}O_2 solution with algal suspension and mixing time appeared to be about 0.2 sec.

The entire apparatus was illuminated from each side by a nine-tube bank of 40-watt fluorescent lights (white) giving a uniform intensity of about 2000 footcandles from each side. During an experiment the algal suspension was illuminated for an hour or more with 4% CO_2 before the start of the flow C^{14} exposures. Exposures to C^{14}O_2 ranging from 1.0 to 16 sec. were then carried out and the products of C^{14}O_2 reduc-

tion analyzed in the usual way[10] by paper chromatography and radioautography.

Short Soybean Experiments.—A single excised trifoliate leaf from a soybean plant (var. *Hawkeye*) was placed in a circular flat illumination chamber with a detachable face. The chamber was equipped with two tubes, the lower one leading through a stopcock to an aspirator and the upper one through a two-way stopcock to a loop containing C^{14}O_2. A loosely tied thread led from the leaf stem under the detachable face gasket, thence through a boiling ethanol bath and a glass tube to a weight. The illumination chamber was partially evacuated, both stopcocks were closed, and clamps removed from the chamber, the detachable face remaining in position through atmospheric pressure. With the opening of the upper stopcock, the C^{14}O_2 was swept into the cham-

(10) A. A. Benson, *et al.*, THIS JOURNAL, **72**, 1710 (1950).

DEGRADATION OF RIBULOSE

$$
\begin{array}{c}
\text{HC}=\text{N}-\overset{\text{H}}{\text{N}}-\text{C}_6\text{H}_5 \\
\text{C}=\text{N}-\text{N}-\text{C}_6\text{H}_5 \\
\overset{\text{H}}{\text{HC}}-\text{OH} \\
\text{HC}-\text{OH} \\
\text{CH}_2\text{OH}
\end{array}
\xrightarrow[\text{NaHCO}_3]{\text{HIO}_4}
\begin{array}{c}
\text{HC}=\text{N}-\overset{\text{H}}{\text{N}}-\text{C}_6\text{H}_5 \\
\text{C}=\text{N}-\text{N}-\text{C}_6\text{H}_5 \\
\overset{\text{H}}{\text{CHO}}
\end{array}
+ \text{HCOOH} + \text{HCHO}
$$

$$1, 2, 3 \qquad\qquad 4 \qquad 5$$

$$
\begin{array}{c}
\text{Phenyl-} \\
\text{hydrazine}
\end{array}
$$

$$
\begin{array}{c}
\text{CH}_2\text{OH} \\
\text{C}=\text{O} \\
\text{HCOH} \\
\text{HCOH} \\
\text{CH}_2\text{OH}
\end{array}
\xrightarrow[\text{H}^+]{\text{Ce(ClO}_4)_6{}^=}
\underset{2}{\text{CO}_2} + 4\text{HCOOH}
$$

$$
\xrightarrow[\text{PtO}_2]{\text{H}_2,}
\begin{array}{c}
\text{CH}_2\text{OH} \\
\text{HCOH} \\
\text{HCOH} \\
\text{HCOH} \\
\text{CH}_2\text{OH}
\end{array}
\xrightarrow{\text{HIO}_4}
\underset{1, 5}{2\text{HCHO}} + \underset{2, 3, 4}{3\text{HCOOH}}
$$

ber by atmospheric pressure, the detachable face fell off and the leaf was pulled into boiling ethanol. An estimated exposure time of 0.4 sec. was obtained. The radioactive products were extracted and analyzed in the usual way. In other experiments, longer exposure times were obtained by holding the detachable face in position.

Degradation of Sugars.—The reactions used for the degradation of the radioactive ribulose and sedoheptulose are shown in the accompany flow sheets.

All radioactive material was purified on two-dimensional paper chromatograms.[10] Radioactive sedoheptulose was converted to the anhydride by heating at 100° with acid-treated Dowex-50 for one hour, followed by chromatography to separate the resulting equilibrium mixture.

Formation of the Osazones.—The hexose and heptose osazones were made in the usual manner with phenylhydrazine hydrochloride, sodium acetate and acetic acid. Usually about 25 mg. of sugar carrier was used for the reaction. Sedoheptulose osazone cocrystallized with glucosazone sufficiently well for fructose to be used as carrier with sedoheptulose activity.

The radioactive arabinosazone was made by the method of Haskins, Hann and Hudson[11] with 10 mg. of arabinose carrier. The osazone was recrystallized once and diluted, as desired for each degradation, with pure crystalline, non-radioactive arabinosazone from a similar large-scale preparation.

Oxidation of Osazones.—The recrystallized osazones were treated with periodate in bicarbonate buffer as described by Topper and Hastings.[12] The reaction mixture was fractionated to obtain all the products by centrifuging and thoroughly washing the mesoxaldehyde osazone; distilling the supernate plus washings to dryness *in vacuo* and treating the distillate with dimedon to obtain the formaldehyde derivative; and acidifying and vacuum distilling the residue to obtain the formic acid, which was counted as barium formate. All products were recrystallized before counting.

Cerate Oxidation of Ketoses.—The oxidation of the carbonyl carbon of a ketose to CO₂ by cerate ion was performed according to the method described by Smith.[13] To a solution of an aliquot portion of radioactivity plus weighed carrier (sedoheptulosan or fructose) was added a slight excess of 0.5 M cerate ion[14] in 6 N perchloric acid, the final concentration of acid being 4 N. The resultant CO₂ was

(11) W. T. Haskins, R. N. Hann and C. S. Hudson, THIS JOURNAL, **68**, 1766 (1946).

(12) Y. J. Topper and A. B. Hastings, *J. Biol. Chem.*, **179**, 1255 (1949).

(13) G. Frederick Smith, "Cerate Oxidimetry," G. Frederick Smith Chemical Company, Columbus, Ohio, 1942.

(14) We are indebted to Prof. John C. Speck, Jr., of Michigan State College, East Lansing, Michigan, for valuable data and suggestions regarding the use of cerate in these oxidations.

swept with nitrogen into CO₂-free sodium hydroxide. The reaction was allowed to proceed for one hour at room temperature and then the CO₂ was precipitated and counted as barium carbonate. In all cases the theoretical amount of carbon dioxide was evolved.

Formation and Oxidation of Sugar Alcohols.—The radioactive sugars were hydrogenated with platinum oxide as described previously[8] and chromatographed on paper for purification. Carrier ribitol or volemitol was added to an aliquot of radioactive alcohol and a slight excess of paraperiodic acid was added. The reaction was allowed to stand at room temperature for 6–7 hours. Then the formic acid and formaldehyde were distilled off *in vacuo*. After the formic acid was titrated with barium hydroxide, the formaldehyde was redistilled and precipitated as formyldimedon. Both the residue of barium formate and the formyldimedon were recrystallized before plating and counting.

Bacterial Oxidation of Hepitols from the Reduction of Sedoheptulose.—The radioactive reduction products of sedoheptulose gave only one spot on chromatography. After elution these were oxidized by *Acetobacter suboxydans* in a small-scale modification of the usual method.[15] Two mg. of volemitol and about 100 μl. of solution of radioactive heptitols were placed in a 7-mm. diameter vial. An amount of yeast extract sufficient to make a 0.5% solution was added. The vial was sterilized, then inoculated from a 24-hour culture of *Acetobacter* and left for a week at room temperature in a humid atmosphere.

When the bacteria were centrifuged from the incubation mixture and the supernatant solution was chromatographed, three radioactive spots were obtained. The two major spots were mannoheptulose and sedoheptulose, the oxidation products of volemitol. The third had R_f values very similar to those of fructose and cochromatographed with authentic guloheptulose[16] (R_f in phenol = 0.47; R_f in butanol-propionic acid-water = 0.24). After treatment with Dowex-50 in the acid form at 100° for one hour, this third compound gave a new compound which cochromatographed with guloheptulosan (R_f in phenol = 0.62; R_f in butanol-propionic acid-water = 0.30). It thus appeared that the radioactive heptitols are volemitol and β-sedoheptitol which cochromatograph in the solvents used.

Both mannoheptulose and guloheptulose have carbon chains inverted from the original sedoheptulose. In the small-scale fermentations, however, the oxidation appeared to be incomplete. The original alcohol did not separate chromatographically from mannoheptulose. Therefore,

(15) (a) L. C. Stewart, N. K. Richtmyer and C. S. Hudson, THIS JOURNAL, **74**, 2206 (1952); (b) we wish to express our appreciation to Dr. R. Clinton Fuller for his development of the micro-fermentation.

(16) We wish to thank Dr. N. K. Richtmyer for his generous gift of crystalline guloheptulosan.

the easily purified guloheptulose was used for subsequent degradations with cerate ion, despite its much poorer yield.

Oxidation of Sedoheptulosan.—The radioactive sample and carrier were treated with sodium periodate as described by Pratt, Richtmyer and Hudson[17] and allowed to stand at room temperature for 3–4 days to give time for most of the formate to be released from the intermediate ester. Then the mixture was acidified with iodic acid and the formic acid was distilled *in vacuo*. This was then counted as barium formate.

Results

In Fig. 2, the radiocarbon fixed in a "steady state" photosynthesis with *Scenedesmus* is shown as a function of time of exposure of the plant to $C^{14}O_2$.

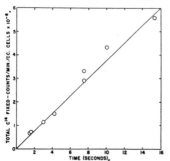

Fig. 2.—Radioactivity incorporated in "steady state" photosynthesis with *Scenedesmus*.

The rate of incorporation of $C^{14}O_2$ appears to be reasonably constant over the period of the experiment. The distribution of radioactivity among various labeled compounds is shown in Fig. 3. The

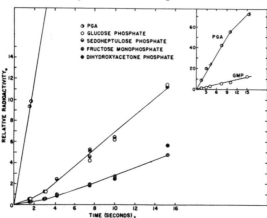

Fig. 3.—Distribution of radioactivity among compounds formed during "steady state" photosynthesis with *Scenedesmus*.

curve for the sugar diphosphates, principally ribulose diphosphate, is not shown but lies between the

(17) J. W. Pratt, N. K. Richtmyer and C. S. Hudson, THIS JOURNAL, **74**, 2200 (1952).

glucose monophosphate and fructose monophosphate curves although individual points are more erratic, probably due to the relative instability of the ribulose diphosphate.[8] The appearance of compounds other than PGA with a finite rate of labeling at the shortest times is demonstrated in Fig. 4 in which the percentage distributions of PGA and of the total sugar phosphates are shown.

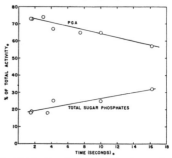

Fig. 4.—Distribution of activity in "steady state" *Scenedesmus*.

The extrapolations of the PGA and sugar phosphates to zero time would give about 75 and 17%, respectively. The remaining 8% not shown is distributed among malic acid (3%), free glyceric acid (2%) and phosphoenolpyruvic acid (3%).[9] The percentage distribution among the sugar phosphates is shown in Fig. 5 where it is seen that no single labeled sugar phosphate predominates at the shortest times.

These data alone do not permit assignment of an order of precedence of the various labeled compounds in the path of carbon reduction. In order to make such an assignment it would be necessary to measure the relative rates of increase in specific activity of the various compounds. If the slopes of the curves shown in Fig. 3 are measured between 2 and 10 sec., rates of increase in total radioactivity are obtained. If these rates are divided by the cellular concentration of the compounds involved, rates of specific activity increase are obtained. This has been done using measurements of concentrations made by two independent[9,18] methods which agreed fairly well in relative order (*i.e.*, PGA concentration: GMP concentration = 4:1). The resulting values ranged from 0.3 for GMP to 1.0 for PGA, with FMP, DHAP, RDP and SMP falling between these values when the rates for these compounds were divided by 2, 1, 2, 1, 1 and 3, respectively, to allow for the number of carbon atoms which degradation data reported be-

(18) A. A. Benson, Z. *Elektrochem*, **56**, 848 (1952).

low show to be labeled significantly at these short times. This calculation is quite approximate, the concentration of compounds involved being measured in experiments with algae photosynthesizing under somewhat different conditions (*i.e.*, 1% CO_2 instead of 4%). However, such a calculation does show more clearly the rapidity with which radiocarbon is distributed among the principally labeled carbon atoms and the difficulty in assigning an order of precedence of labeled compounds on the basis of labeling rates alone.

The fact that compounds besides PGA have finite initial labeling slopes (which results in their percentage activity not extrapolating to zero at zero time) might be explained in several ways. One possibility is that during the killing time some of the enzymatic reactions (in this case reduction of PGA and rearrangement of the sugars) may not be stopped as suddenly as others (the carboxylation to give PGA) or may even be accelerated by the rising temperature prior to enzyme denaturation.

Another explanation is that some of the labeled molecules may be passed from enzyme to enzyme without completely equilibrating with the active reservoirs which are actually being measured. This sort of enzymatic transfer of radiocarbon could invalidate precedence assignments based on rates of increase in specific activities since the reservoirs would no longer be completely in the line of carbon transfer. That the equilibration between reservoirs and enzyme–substrate complexes is rapid compared to the carbon reduction cycle as a whole is indicated by the fact that all the reservoirs become appreciably labeled before there is an appreciable label in the α- and β-carbons of PGA, the 1-, 2-, 5- and 6-carbons of the hexoses, etc. In any event, it would appear to be safer to establish the reaction sequences from qualitative differences in labeling within molecules (degradation data) and changes in reservoir sizes due to controlled changes in one environmental variable rather than from quantitative interpretations of labeling rate data.

Table I shows the results of degradations on sugars obtained from the soybean series. The first column shows the variation in labeling of carbon

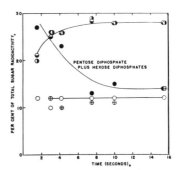

Fig. 5.—Distribution of radioactivity incorporated in "steady state" photosynthesis with *Scenedesmus*: ◐, sedoheptulose phosphate; ◑, glucose phosphate; ⊕, dihydroxyacetone phosphate; O, fructose phosphate.

since the carbon dioxide is depleted just prior to the administration of $C^{14}O_2$. Included in the table is a complete degradation of a sedoheptulose sample from *Sedum spectabile* grown in radioactive carbon dioxide for two days (kindly supplied by N. E. Tolbert, Oak Ridge National Laboratory). Assuming this sample is uniformly labeled, its degradation indicates the probable limits of accuracy of the other degradations—about $\pm 10\%$ of the obtained value, mainly due to plating and counting errors resulting from the low amount of radioactivity available for degradation. The five degradations on sedoheptulose make it possible to obtain separate values for all the carbon atoms. Although the carbon-fourteen labels of carbon atoms 1 and 6 were not determined in the case of the *Scenedesmus* experiments, they were assumed small and approximately equal to carbon-fourteen labels found in carbons 2 and 7, by analogy with the soybean leaf experiments where the labels of all carbon atoms of the sedoheptulose were determined. The label in each carbon atom of the ribulose can be obtained individually from the three degradations performed. The distributions in Table II should be interpreted as a clear qualitative picture of the position of the radioactivity within the molecule rather than as a

TABLE I

Radioactivity Distribution in Sugars Sedoheptulose and Hexose from Soybean Leaves

Time, sec.	Sedoheptulose							Hexose	
	C-4	C-1,2,3	C-4,5,6	C-7	C-2	C-1,7	C-6	C-1,2,3	C-4,5,6
0.4	8	32	57	0				47	52
0.8	18	43	60	2				48	51
1.5	24								
3.5	26				3				
5.0	29	36	64	2	4	4	4		
8.0	24								
10.0	28								
20.0	21	41	..	5	7				
300	14				12.5				
Sedum	12	37	35	12	12.5	28	15		

number four of sedoheptulose obtained from soybean leaves exposed to $C^{14}O_2$ for very short periods. These soybean leaf experiments are, of course, not intended to represent "steady state" photosynthesis

TABLE II

Radioactivity Distribution in Compounds from Flow Experiments (Algae)

	5.4 Seconds			8.5 Seconds	
Glyceric acid	Fructose	Sedoheptulose	Ribulose	Sedoheptulose	Ribulose
		2			
	3	2		3	
	3	28	11		11
	43	24	10	22	11
82	42	27	69		64
6	3	2	5		8
6	3	2	3		5

quantitative picture. Fewer points were taken in this "steady state" flow experiment than in the one described earlier in order to obtain more labeled sugar per point for degradation purposes.

In other experiments[19] the *Scenedesmus* have been kept at a steady state of light, temperature, CO_2 pressure, etc., and constant $C^{14}O_2$ specific activity until successive samplings of the suspensions showed uniform labeling ("saturation") of all the common photosynthetic reservoirs (PGA, RDP, GMP, etc.). The total CO_2 pressure was then rapidly changed from 1% CO_2-in-air to 0.003% in air, all other environmental conditions, including the specific activity of $C^{14}O_2$, being kept constant. The conditions of this experiment were, therefore, similar to those used previously[9] to study changing steady state except that CO_2 pressure was changed instead of illumination. In the case where the CO_2 pressure was lowered (Fig. 6), the initial effects on the reservoir sizes of PGA and RDP were just the opposite of those observed when the illumination was stopped. Lowered CO_2 pressure resulted in an

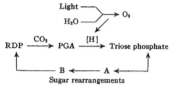

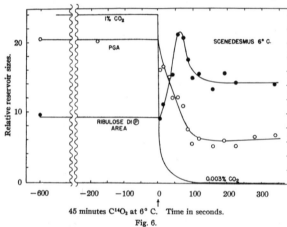

45 minutes $C^{14}O_2$ at 6° C.   Time in seconds.

Fig. 6.

increase in the reservoir size of RDP and a decrease in that of the PGA. After a time the reservoir of RDP passed through a maximum and dropped to a lower level but the new steady state RDP reservoir was now greater relative to that of PGA. The labeled glycolic acid present, though rather a small percentage of total activity, increased many fold when the CO_2 pressure was lowered. The reservoir of glycolic acid increased much more slowly than that of the RDP and did not pass through a corresponding maximum, thus eliminating the possibility that most of the labeled glycolic acid was formed by thermal decomposition of RDP subsequent to killing of the cells.

Discussion

1. Origin of PGA.—It has been suggested that RDP is the compound which supplies the two-carbon atoms for the carboxylation reaction leading to PGA.[9] If the reactions of these compounds are represented by

then the initial changes in reservoir sizes which would accompany changes in light or CO_2 pressure can be predicted. When the light is turned off, reducing power [H] decreases, so the reservoir of PGA would increase and that of RDP decrease. If CO_2 pressure decreases, then the reservoir of RDP would increase and that of PGA would decrease. Both effects, as well as those opposite effects which would be expected to accompany a resumption of light or increase in CO_2 pressure, have been observed. These results support the proposal of a carboxylation of RDP to give two molecules of PGA or the reductive carboxylation to give one molecule of PGA and one of phosphoglyceraldehyde as the first step in the path of carbon dioxide reduction.

It is also possible that the products of this carboxylation may be phosphoglyceraldehyde and 3-phosphohydroxypyruvate. In this case subsequent reduction of the phosphohydroxypyruvate would give first PGA and then phosphoglyceraldehyde. The reaction of phosphoglyceraldehyde with hydroxypyruvate to give ribulose monophosphate and CO_2 has been demonstrated by Racker[20] to take place under the influence of the transketolase enzyme. However, the increase in PGA concentration which is observed on stopping the illumination of photosynthesizing algae,[9] would probably not be seen if a reduction of hydroxypyruvate were required to form PGA since the reducing agent would presumably no longer be formed in the dark. Moreover, paper chromatographic analysis should detect either phosphohydroxypyruvate or its decarboxylation product, phosphoglycolaldehyde, and neither have been found in our experiments. When C^{14}-labeled hydroxypyruvate was administered to algae in this Laboratory, the labeled acid was metabolized to give a variety of compounds, similar to those formed from labeled pyruvate or acetate, which were related more closely to the tricarboxylic acid cycle and fat synthesis than to the compounds usually associated with carbon reduction in photosynthesis.

There remains the possibility that the RDP first splits to give a three-carbon molecule and a free two-carbon fragment which is then carboxylated.

(19) A. T. Wilson, Thesis, to be submitted as partial fulfillment of requirements for the degree of Doctor of Philosophy, University of California.

(20) E. Racker, G. de la Haba and I. G. Leder, THIS JOURNAL, **75**, 1010 (1953).

However, if the glycolic acid is an indication of the free two-carbon fragment, then the observation that its increase in concentration (following reduction in CO_2 pressure) is not as rapid as the increase in RDP concentration suggests that the C_2 compound is not as closely related to the carboxylation reaction as the RDP.

2. Origin of Ribulose Diphosphate.—If one considers the principal labeling at short times of PGA,[2] RDP, SMP and the two hexose monophosphates[2] as, respectively

CH_2OP	$*CH_2OP$	CH_2OH	C
$CHOH$	$*C=O$	$C=O$	C
$***COOH$	$***CHOH$	$*CHOH$	$*C$
	$CHOH$	$*CHOH$	$*C$
	CH_2OP	$*CHOH$	C
		$CHOH$	C
		CH_2OP	
PGA	RDP	SMP	HMP

it appears that the ribulose is not derived entirely from a $C_6 \rightarrow C_1 + C_5$ split or a $C_7 \rightarrow C_2 + C_5$ split. No five carbon fragment of the hexose or the heptose molecules contains the same distribution of radiocarbon as ribulose. The combination of C_3 with a labeled C_2 fragment could account for the observed radioactivity. However, some mechanism for the labeling of the C_2 fragment would be required. One such mechanism would be the breakdown of hexose simultaneously into three C_2 fragments,[21] and since carbon atoms 3 and 4 of hexose are labeled, a labeled C_2 fragment might thus be obtained. To our knowledge there exists no precedent as yet for this type of reaction.

Another way of accounting for the observed distribution of radioactivity which seems quite plausible in view of the rapidly accumulating enzymatic evidence for the reverse reaction[20,22-24] is the formation of ribulose from sedoheptulose and triose. This reaction could result in the observed labeling

CH_2OH	$**CHO$	CH_2OH	$*CHO$	$*C$
$C=O$ +	$CHOH$ →	$C=O$ +	$*CHOH$	$*C$
$*CHOH$	CH_2OP	$**CHOH$	$*CHOH$	$***C$
$*CHOH$		$CHOH$	$CHOH$	C
$*CHOH$		CH_2OP	CH_2OP	C
$CHOH$				
CH_2OP	phospho-	ribulose	ribose	
SMP	glyceraldehyde	monophos-	monophos-	
		phate	phate	

If the ribose-5-phosphate and ribulose-5-phosphate are then converted to RDP the resulting distribu-

(21) H. Gaffron, E. W. Fager and J. L. Rosenberg, "Carbon Dioxide Fixation and Photosynthesis," Symposia of the Society for Experimental Biology (Great Britain), Vol. V, Cambridge University Press, 1951.

(22) B. Axelrod, R. S. Bandurski, C. M. Greiner and R. Jang, *J. Biol. Chem.*, **202**, 619 (1953).

(23) B. L. Horecker and P. Z. Smyrniotis, THIS JOURNAL, **74**, 2123 (1952).

(24) B. L. Horecker and P. Z. Smyrniotis, *ibid.*, **75**, 1009 (1953).

tion of label would be that observed (carbon skeleton at right of reaction).

3. Origin of Sedoheptulose.—The degradation data appear to eliminate the possibility of formation of sedoheptulose by a simple $6 + 1$ or $5 + 2$ addition, if we assume that no special reservoirs of pentose and hexose exist with distributions of radioactivity different from those measured. A reverse of the reactions proposed above for formation of RDP would require segregation of ribose and ribulose distributions as well as some other mechanism for labeling the ribose in the manner shown. It does seem likely that all the reactions involving rearrangements of sugars and perhaps those involving reduction of PGA as well are at least partially reversible in the time of these experiments. If all these compounds are intermediates in a cycle of carbon reduction, then during steady state photosynthesis there will be a net "flow" of radiocarbon in the "forward" direction, but the possibility that the distribution of radiocarbon in later intermediates may reflect to some extent that of earlier intermediates cannot be entirely ignored.

The condensation of a triose with a C_4 fragment would give the observed distribution if the C_4 fragment is labeled in the carbon atoms 1 and 2

CH_2OP	$[*CHO]$		CH_2OP
$C=O$ +	$*CHOH$	→	$C=O$
$*CH_2OH$	$CHOH$		$*CHOH$
	CH_2OP		$*CHOH$
			$*CHOH$
			$CHOH$
DHAP			CH_2OP

Enzymatic evidence for this reaction and its reverse has been reported.[23,25]

4. Origin of the Four-Carbon Fragment.—Two possible modes of formation of the four-carbon fragment with the above labeling are a $C_1 + C_3$ addition, and a $C_6 \rightarrow [C_2] + [C_4]$ split. The $C_1 + C_3$ addition which leads to malic acid produces a C_4 fragment labeled in the two terminal positions.[6] Therefore, the reduction of the dicarboxylic acid formed as a precursor to malic acid could not result in a C_4 fragment with the C^{14} distribution required for the formation of 3,4,5-C^{14} labeled sedoheptulose. The rapid introduction of radiocarbon into malic acid in earlier experiments[4] can be accounted for if it is assumed that the reservoir size of malic acid, depleted during the air flushing prior to the addition of $HC^{14}O_3^-$, was increasing after the addition of radiocarbon due to the increase in total CO_2 pressure. Also, after the carboxyl group of PGA and phosphoenolpyruvic acid have become appreciably labeled, the malic acid is doubly labeled.

It is interesting to note that in the long term "steady state" experiments in which the light was turned off,[9] the malic acid concentration dropped when the light was turned off rather than increasing as PGA concentration increased. If malic acid were an indicator of a four-carbon intermediate in carbon reduction, the product of a second carboxyl-

(25) B. L. Horecker and P. Z. Smyrniotis, *ibid.*, **75**, 2021 (1953).

ation, then one would expect its concentration to increase in the dark for two reasons. First, there no longer is reducing power which would reduce the carboxylation product to sugar if this product were an intermediate in CO_2 reduction. Second, the rate of formation of malic acid should increase since this rate depends on the CO_2 concentration (which remains constant), and the concentration of phosphoenolpyruvic acid (which increases paralleling the PGA concentration). The decrease in malic acid concentration could be easily explained on the basis of the proposed light inhibition of pyruvic acid oxidation.[9] The cessation of illumination should permit increased pyruvic acid oxidation, thus providing more acetyl–CoA, which can react with oxaloacetic acid derived from malic acid.

It is possible that there is a different "second carboxylation" $(C_3 + C_1)$ leading eventually to a four-carbon fragment which can react with triose to give sedoheptulose, but there seems to be no evidence whatever for such a reaction at present. Moreover, such a reaction should lead in short times to a four-carbon fragment somewhat more labeled in the terminal carbon position than in the second carbon position due to dilution of the carbon introduced in the first carboxylation reaction by the PGA and triose reservoirs. This is not the case—in fact in the very shortest times the terminal carbon position of the hypothetical C_4 fragment (carbon four of sedoheptulose) is actually less labeled than the second position, at least in the soybean experiments.

The most likely source of the C_4 fragment seems to be a $C_6 \rightarrow [C_4] + [C_2]$ split. Trioses could then react with $[C_4]$ and $[C_2]$ to give sedoheptulose and ribulose, respectively. One possible formulation of these reactions would be

The first reaction as written above would be a transketolase reaction of the type reported by Racker, et al.,[20] who found that this enzyme splits ribulose-5-phosphate, leaving glyceraldehyde-3-phosphate and transferring the remaining two carbon atoms to an acceptor aldehyde phosphate of 2-, 3- or 5-carbon atoms. No mention was made of the effect of transketolase on ribulose-5-phosphate with erythrose-4-phosphate which would result in

the formation of fructose phosphate by a reaction which is just the reverse of the $C_6 \rightarrow [C_2] + [C_4]$ split written above.[26]

The labeling of carbon number 4 in sedoheptulose observed in the case of the very short periods of photosynthesis with soybean leaves seems to cast some doubt on the $C_6 \rightarrow [C_2] + [C_4]$ split unless one can assume that the C_6 which splits is itself not symmetrically labeled at the shortest times, due to different specific activities of the two trioses which react to give hexose

Degradation of fructose from the 0.4- and 0.3-sec. experiments showed no significant difference between the two halves of fructose. It is quite possible, however, that the differences in denaturation rates of various enzymes mentioned earlier may influence the results in these short times.

Combining these reactions with others already proposed we have the following cyclic path of carbon reduction during photosynthesis. The carbon fragments specified only by the number of carbon atoms in their chains are all at the sugar level of reduction

$$3C_5 + 3CO_2 \longrightarrow 6PGA$$
$$6PGA \xrightarrow{12[H]} 6C_3$$
$$2C_3 \longrightarrow C_6$$
$$C_6 + 2C_3 \longrightarrow C_5 + C_7$$
$$C_7 + C_3 \longrightarrow 2C_5$$

The net reaction for each turn of the cycle is

$$12[H] + 3CO_2 \longrightarrow C_3H_6O_3 + 3H_2O$$

The operation of this cycle is illustrated in Fig. 7.

5. Energetics of the Carbon Reduction Cycle.— That the enzymatic rearrangements of sugars requires no additional supply of energy in the form of ATP or other sources seems to be indicated by the experiments with isolated and partially purified enzyme preparations in which such rearrangements have been carried out without the addition of energy donors. The free energy change of the carboxylation reaction can be roughly estimated. Estimating the free energy difference between ribose-

(26) Since this was written, a private communication from Dr. Racker has informed us that he has observed this reaction with F-6-P

100

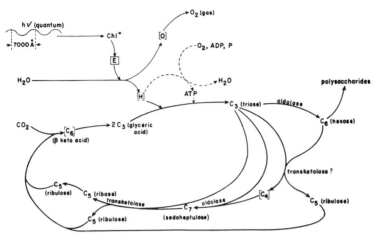

Fig. 7.—Proposed cycle for carbon reduction in photosynthesis. Heavy lines indicate transformations of carbon compounds, light lines the path of conversion of radiant energy to chemical energy and the subsequent use of this energy stored momentarily in some compound (E), to form a reducing agent [H] and oxygen from water.

5-phosphate and RDP equal to that between GMP and fructose diphosphate, the free energy change for the reaction below is about -7 kcal.[27,28]

$$\begin{array}{c}CH_2O\textcircled{P}\\ |\\ C=O\\ |\\ CHOH\\ |\\ CHOH\\ |\\ CHOH\\ |\\ CH_2O\textcircled{P}\end{array} + CO_2 + H_2O \longrightarrow 2\begin{array}{c}CH_2O\textcircled{P}\\ |\\ CHOH\\ |\\ CO_2\end{array} + 2H^+$$

$$\begin{array}{cccccc}(5 \times 10^{-4}\,M) & (10^{-2}\,M) & & (1.4 \times 10^{-3}M) & (10^{-7}\,M)\\ \Delta F \quad 2\textcircled{P} \;-176 & -95 & -57 \to & 2(\textcircled{P}\;-158) & 2(-95)\\ & & & \Delta F = -7 \text{ kcal.}\end{array}$$

In the above calculation the concentrations of RDP and PGA measured with *Scenedesmus* during photosynthesis with 1% CO_2[9] are used. The mechanism of the reaction may consist of the addition of CO_2 to the 2,3-enediol sugar formed by enolization of the RDP. The intermediate compound would be 2-carboxypentulose-3. The free energy for the formation of the ion of this acid and H^+ (pH 7) from CO_2 and RDP is estimated as zero when the concentration of the intermediate acid is $10^{-9}\,M$. Subsequent hydrolytic splitting of this compound to two molecules of PGA and another hydrogen ion would proceed with a free energy change of -7 kcal.

The energy required to maintain the operation of the proposed carbon reduction cycle might be supplied entirely in the reduction of PGA to triose phosphate. If this reduction were accomplished by a reversal of the enzymatic reaction usually writ-

(27) The internal energy of the $-PO_4H^-$ group, exclusive of the energy of bonding to the remainder of the molecule is here denoted by $\textcircled{P}$ and assumed constant throughout.

(28) J. A. Bassham, Thesis, submitted as partial fulfillment of requirements for the degree of Doctor of Philosophy, University of California, 1949.

ten, each "turn" of the cycle would be represented by three times the reaction

$$2DPN[H_2] + 2ATP + CO_2 \longrightarrow \{CH_2O\} + \qquad (A)$$
$$+ 2DPN + 2ADP + 2\textcircled{P} + H_2O$$

This is the sum of the reactions

$$\begin{array}{ll}2[DPN[H_2] + \frac{1}{2}O_2 \longrightarrow & \\ \quad DPN + H_2O] & \Delta F = -101 \text{ kcal.} \quad (B)\\ 2[ATP \longrightarrow ADP + \textcircled{P}] & \Delta F = -21 \text{ kcal.} \quad (C)\\ CO_2 + H_2O \longrightarrow O_2 + \{CH_2O\} & \Delta F = +116 \text{ kcal.} \quad (D)\end{array}$$

The efficiency of the transfer of energy of reactions B and C to reaction D is $116/(21 + 101) = 0.96$.

However, additional energy might be supplied to the operation of the cycle by phosphorylation reactions in which additional molecules of ATP are required. One such reaction may well be the phosphorylation of ribulose monophosphate to give ribulose diphosphate. In this case, one additional molecule of ATP would be required per molecule of CO_2 reduced. The efficiency of the net reaction (A') would then be $116/132.5 = 0.88$.

$$2DPN[H_2] + 3ATP + CO_2 \longrightarrow$$
$$\{CH_2O\} + 2DPN + 3ADP + 3\textcircled{P} + H_2O \quad (A')$$

The over-all efficiency of photosynthesis would be the product of 0.96 or 0.88 and the efficiency of the process by which water is photolyzed to give oxygen with the production of reducing power, followed by the conversion of the energy of this reducing power to DPN[H$_2$] and ATP.

If the mechanism for photolysis of water involves thioctic acid, as has been proposed,[29] the energetics of the photochemical and following steps can be estimated

$$\underset{S-S}{\boxed{\bigwedge}} + HOH \xrightarrow{h\nu} \underset{SH \; SOH}{\bigwedge} \qquad (E)$$

(29) J. A. Barltrop, P. M. Hayes and M. Calvin, to be published.

(where the symbol / represents the side chain: $-(CH_2)_4CO_2H$).

$$2SH \; SOH \longrightarrow SH \; SH + S-S + H_2O + \tfrac{1}{2}O_2 \quad (F)$$

In this process, two quanta are required for each dithiol molecule formed. The stored energy is the sum of the energies of the two half reactions

$$H_2O \longrightarrow 2H^+ + 2e^- + \tfrac{1}{2}O_2 \quad \Delta F = +37.5 \text{ kcal.} \quad (G)$$

$$S-S + 2H^+ + 2e^- \longrightarrow HS \; SH \quad \begin{array}{l} E = -0.3 \text{ v.}[30] \\ \Delta F = +13.8 \text{ kcal.} \end{array} \quad (H)$$

which is

$$H_2O + S-S \xrightarrow{(2h\nu)} HS \; SH + \tfrac{1}{2}O_2 \quad \Delta F = 51.3 \text{ kcal.} \quad (I)$$

Since the energy available from two light quanta at 7000 Å. is 2×40.7 or 81.4 kcal., the efficiency of this process is $51.3/81.4 = 0.63$.

If Co-I is used in the reduction of PGA, the reduced coenzyme could be formed with high efficiency from the dithiol

$$DPN + SH \; SH \longrightarrow DPN[H_2] + S-S \quad \Delta F = -0.8 \text{ kcal.} \quad (J)$$

The required ATP could be formed in some way by oxidation of $SH \; SH$ or $DPN[H_2]$ by an energetic coupling of the reactions

$$DPN[H_2] + \tfrac{1}{2}O_2 \longrightarrow DPN + H_2O \quad \Delta F = -50.5 \text{ kcal.} \quad (K)$$

$$ADP + \circled{P} \longrightarrow ATP \quad \Delta F = +10.5 \text{ kcal.} \quad (L)$$

Since from one to four molecules of ATP might be formed per $DPN[H_2]$ oxidized, a wide range of efficiencies would be possible. A value of three has been suggested[31] and if this is used, the resulting coupling reaction could be written

$$DPN[H_2] + \tfrac{1}{2}O_2 + 3ADP + 3\circled{P} \longrightarrow DPN + H_2O + 3ATP \quad (M)$$

Multiplying reaction J by 3 and combining with reaction M we have

$$3SH \; SH + 2DPN + 3ADP + 3\circled{P} + \tfrac{1}{2}O_2 \longrightarrow$$

$$+ 2DPN[H_2] + 3ATP + H_2O + 3S-S \quad (N)$$

in which the stored energy is 132.5 kcal. and the energy expended is three times reaction I = 154 kcal. The efficiency of the energy transfers represented by reaction N is then $132.5/154 = 0.86$.

Combining the efficiencies of reactions A', I and N results in a calculated over-all efficiency for photosynthesis of $0.88 \times 0.63 \times 0.86 = 0.48$. Since the mechanism outlined above would require six quanta for each molecule of carbon dioxide reduced (two quanta for each molecule of dithiol used in reaction N) this efficiency can be obtained directly from the energy of these quanta (244 kcal.) and the energy of reaction D: $116/244 = 0.48$.

Higher apparent efficiencies would be obtained at low light intensities where the dark internal conversion of prior storage products (involving no net uptake of oxygen or evolution of CO_2) would supply appreciable amounts of ATP, DPNH, reduced thioctic acid and possibly intermediates of the O_2 evolution chain as well.[27]

Since reaction I as written stores only 51.3 kcal. of 81.4 kcal. available, it is possible that some mechanism may exist for the storage of some of this energy in the form of either additional reducing power or high energy phosphate. In this case, the over-all efficiency would be higher.

6. Other Biological Evidence.—The interconversions of the five-, six- and seven-carbon sugars are being investigated by several laboratories. The postulated cyclic reactions which our data suggest are consistent with the observations of these various groups. Both the work of Axelrod, et al.,[32] with spinach preparations and the results reported by Dische and Pollaczek[32] with hemolysates demonstrate the sequence

ribose phosphate $\longrightarrow$ heptulose phosphate +
triose phosphate $\longrightarrow$ hexose phosphate

Recently studies have been made of the distribution of C^{14} in products resulting from conversion of $1\text{-}C^{14}$ labeled pentoses. Neish[33] has studied the products of bacterial metabolism of several pentoses while Wolin, et al.,[34] investigated the products of enzymatic conversion of ribose-5-phosphate. In both cases, the distribution of radioactivity in the products could be accounted for by a reversal of the reactions herein suggested, although a limited number of other interpretations of their data are possible.

Berkeley, Cal.

(30) I. C. Gunsalus, Symposium on "Mechanism of Enzyme Action," McCollum–Pratt Institute, Johns Hopkins University, 1953, to be published.

(31) A. L. Lehninger, "Phosphorus Metabolism," Vol. I, Johns Hopkins University Press, 1951, page 344.

(32) Z. Dische and E. Pollaczek, paper presented at Second International Congress of Biochemistry, Paris, France, 1952.

(33) A. C. Neish, paper presented at American Society of Bacteriologists Meeting, San Francisco, Calif., 1953.

(34) H. B. Wolin, B. L. Horecker, M. Gibbs and H. Klenow, paper presented at Meeting of American Institute of Biological Sciences, Madison, Wisconsin, 1953.

DYNAMICS OF THE PHOTOSYNTHESIS OF CARBON COMPOUNDS

I. CARBOXYLATION REACTIONS

J. A. BASSHAM AND MARTHA KIRK

Lawrence Radiation Laboratory, University of California, Berkeley, Calif. (U.S.A.)

(Received January 30th, 1960)

SUMMARY

Kinetic studies have been made of the rates of appearance of ^{14}C in individual compounds formed by *Chlorella pyrenoidosa* during steady state photosynthesis with $^{14}CO_2$. These rates have been compared with rates of CO_2 and ^{14}C disappearance from the gas phase during the same experiments.

The following results were obtained:

1. After the first few seconds, the rate of appearance of ^{14}C in compounds stable to drying on planchets at room temperature is 95 to 100 % of the rate of uptake of carbon from the gas phase.

2. After the first few seconds, the rate of appearance of carbon in compounds isolable by usual methods of paper chromatography constitutes at least 73 to 88 % of the rate of uptake of carbon from the gas phase. Compounds formed from the carbon reduction cycle via the carboxylation of ribulose diphosphate account for a least 70 to 85 % of the uptake, while carboxylation of phosphoenolpyruvic acid appears to account for at least another 3 %.

3. The induction period in the appearance of ^{14}C in stable compounds may be due to a reservoir of intracellular CO_2 and HCO_3^- or to some other volatile or unstable compound. If so, this reservoir contains no more than 1.5 μmoles of carbon, corresponding to about 7 sec carbon fixation in the experiment in which it was measured.

4. No other carboxylation reactions, such as the carboxylation of γ-aminobutyric acid, could be observed. The rate of labeling of glutamic acid after 5 min of exposure of the algae to $^{14}CO_2$ reached a maximum rate of about 5 % of the total uptake rate, but this labeling appears to be due to conversion of labeled intermediates formed from the carbon reduction cycle or phosphoenolpyruvic acid carboxylation.

5. The *in vivo* carboxylation of ribulose diphosphate in the light appears to be followed by conversion of the product to one molecule of phosphoglyceric acid, containing the newly incorporated $^{14}CO_2$ and one molecule of some other (kinetically distinguishable) three carbon compound. This reaction would be different from the one reported for the isolated enzyme system and the *in vivo* reaction in the dark, which produces two molecules of 3-phosphoglyceric acid.

Abbreviations: PGA or 3-PGA, 3-phosphoglyceric acid; PEPA, phosphoenolpyruvic acid; RuDP, ribulose 1,5-diphosphate; ATP, adenosine triphosphate; TPNH, reduced triphosphopyridine nucleotide.

INTRODUCTION

Much of the biochemical pathway through which carbon dioxide is reduced during photosynthesis in algae has been established[1-3]. A principal feature of this pathway is the carbon reduction cycle. A simplified version of this cycle is given in Fig. 1, which shows the key steps.

To map these paths, CALVIN *et al.*[3-10] gave radioactive compounds, such as $^{14}CO_2$ and $KH_2{}^{32}PO_4$, to photosynthesizing plants. The plants made various reduced organic compounds from these labeled substrates. They were then killed and the soluble compounds were extracted from the plant material and analyzed by two-dimensional paper chromatography and radioautography. The compounds were identified and their radioactive content determined. From the amount and location of radioactive elements within compounds following exposures of the plants for various lengths of time and under various environmental conditions, biochemical pathways were followed.

Fig. 1. Carbon reduction cycle (simplified version). (1) Ribulose diphosphate reacts with CO_2 to

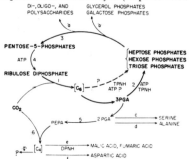

give an unstable six carbon compound which splits to give two three carbon compounds. At least one of these is 3-phosphoglyceric acid. The other three carbon compounds might be either 3-PGA, as it is known to be in the isolated enzyme system, or some other three carbon compound such as a triose phosphate (dashed arrow). (2) PGA is reduced to triose phosphate with ATP and TPNH derived from the light reaction and water. (3) Various condensations and re-arrangements convert the triose phosphates to pentose phosphates. (4) Pentose phosphate is phosphorylated with ATP to give ribulose diphosphate. Further carbon reduction occurs *via* conversion of PGA to phosphoenolpyruvic acid, (5), and carboxylation, (6), to form a four carbon compound (probably oxaloacetic acid). Reactions leading to the formations of some of the secondary intermediates in carbon reduction are shown by the arrows lettered a through g.

In the present study we have extended our information about these pathways by more precise control of the environmental conditions during exposure of the plants to tracers. At the same time we have made measurements of the rate of entry of tracer into the plant and of the rate of appearance of the tracer in specific compounds.

We sought answers to the following questions: (a) How much of the total carbon taken up by the plants enters the metabolic network via carboxylation of ribulose diphosphate (reaction 1)? (b) How much of the total carbon taken up enters by carboxylation of PEPA (reaction 6)? (c) Are any other carboxylation reactions, such as the carboxylation of γ-aminobutyric acid[11], of any importance in steady state photosynthesis? (d) Does the carboxylation of ribulose diphosphate *in vivo* lead to one product only (PGA) or does it lead to two products (PGA and some other 3-carbon compound)?

"Steady state photosynthesis" as used in this paper, is defined as a condition under which unicellular algae are carrying out the reaction of photosynthesis, are synthesizing all of the normal cell constituents, and are growing and dividing at constant rates during the course of the experiment. Moreover, the rates of photosynthesis in experiments which will be reported here were between 30 and 80 % of the maximum rates at which these algae are capable of photosynthesizing at room temperature.

EXPERIMENTAL

Plant material

The plants used in all experiments were the unicellular green algae, *Chlorella pyrenoidosa*, raised in continuous automatic culture tubes as described previously[3]. The algae were raised and harvested as a 0.5 % (volume wet packed cells/volume) suspension. The algae were centrifuged from the culture medium and then suspended in a special nutrient solution (described later). This suspension (80 ml) was placed in the illumination chamber of the steady state apparatus.

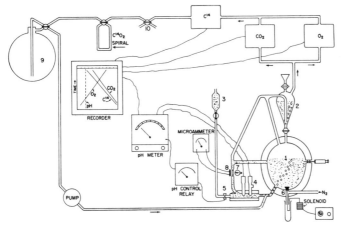

Fig. 2. Steady state apparatus. (1) algae chamber, (2) water or nutrient solution reservoir, (3) acid or base reservoir, (4) pH electrodes, (5) solenoid operated pH control valve, (6) solenoid operated sampling valve, (7) small lamp, (8) photovoltaic cell, (9) large gas reservoir, (10) four-way stopcock.

Steady state apparatus

In the steady state apparatus, shown schematically in Fig. 2, a stream of gas (1 to 2 % CO_2 in air) is cycled through a closed system. The gas is bubbled through the 0.5 % or 1.0 % suspension of algae (80 ml) at a rate of approximately 1 l/min. Gas and liquid mix rapidly in the algae chamber, which is 3/8'' thick and 4'' in diameter (inside dimensions). The algae chamber is illuminated from both sides by G.E. RSP2 photospot incandescent lights through an infrared absorbing glass in a water bath, or in some experiments from one side by an incandescent lamp and from the other side by a bank of eight 8'', 6 W fluorescent lamps (blue and cool white). In either case, the voltage to the incandescent lamps is adjusted just to give light saturation of the oxygen evolution rate. The algae chamber is water jacketed, and the water is circulated in a thermostated bath. The temperature of this bath is set so that during steady state photosynthesis the temperature indicated by the thermometer in the algae suspension reads $25°$.

The algae chamber is connected to a side loop through which the algae suspension is made to circulate by the flow of gas into the chamber. A beam from a small lamp passes through a window in the side loop to a photovoltaic cell which measures the light absorption and hence the density of the algae. Electrodes in the side loop measure pH, which is recorded on a multipoint recorder. The pH meter output is also connected to a control relay which, through the activation of a solenoid-operated valve, can cause acid or base from a reservoir to be added in small volumes to the algal suspension. Another reservoir within the closed system contains distilled water or nutrient solution, which can be added to the algal suspension to dilute it to the selected concentration as the algae grow.

A solenoid-operated sampling valve at the bottom of the chamber permits one to take 1-ml samples rapidly (every 2 sec if desired). The inside of the algal chamber is maintained at slightly above atmospheric pressure to force the algal sample out of the chamber. When samples of algae are taken, they are run into 4 ml of methanol at room temperature. This gives a mixture which contains about 80 % methanol by volume. No significant difference in the resulting labeling pattern is seen whether the algae are killed this way, in boiling ethanol, or in ethanol kept at $-40°$.

After the gas in the closed system bubbles through the algae, it passes through instruments which measure CO_2, ^{14}C, and O_2, and each measurement is automatically recorded. From the known sensitivities of these instruments and the volume of the system, one can calculate rates of exchange of these quantities and specific radioactivity. A large reservoir and small reservoirs may be connected or disconnected from the closed system to obtain closed systems of various sizes. The volume of the largest system is 6400 ml, while the volume of the smallest system is 435 ml. The system can be open during the pre-labeling period by means of a stopcock.

Nutrient solution

For steady state experiments it is necessary to supply the algae with all the inorganic compounds required for them to photosynthesize and grow at a normal rate. Unfortunately, the nutrient solution in which they are usually grown in the laboratory contains quantities of salts which make impossible an adequate separation of labeled compounds by two-dimensional paper chromatography. Therefore, the algae are suspended in much more dilute nutrient solutions of which that in Table I is typical.

TABLE I

STARTING NUTRIENT SOLUTION FOR STEADY STATE EXPTS. 18 AND 28

$(NH_4)_2HPO_4$	40 mg/l
$MgSO_4 \cdot 7H_2O$	20 mg/l
NH_4Cl	20 mg/l
KNO_3	20 mg/l
ARNON's A-4 solution of trace elements plus	
$\quad CoCl_2 \cdot 6H_2O$ (40 mg/l) and MoO_3 (15 mg/l)[12]	1 ml/l
Fe^{++}-versenol solution to give 90 mM Fe^{++}	1 ml/l
NH_4VO_3 (23 mg/l)	1 ml/l

This medium was adequate to maintain nearly a constant rate of photosynthesis in experiment steady state No. 18. In other experiments, such as steady state 28, the algae growing under steady state conditions would in time exhaust the supply of ammonium ion contained in this medium. However, it has been observed that as the algae take up ammonium ion, the pH of the medium tends to decrease, presumably due to the exchange into the medium of hydrogen ions for ammonium ions. Therefore, dilute NH_4OH was added to the algae suspension automatically by the pH control system, thereby maintaining constant pH. At the same time ammonium ion concentration was maintained approximately constant. The nutrient solution for pH control was diluted by trial and error until its addition kept the algae density constant. To it were added other inorganic ions in a ratio to the ammonium ion which was estimated to provide the algae with an adequate level of these ions for growth for a limited period. The resulting pH control medium used in steady state experiment 28 is shown in Table II.

TABLE II

CONTROL MEDIUM USED IN STEADY STATE EXPERIMENT 28

$(NH_4)HPO_4$	6.6 mg/l
$(NH_4)_2SO_4$	6.6 mg/l
NH_4OH	0.55 mg/l
$FeCl_3 \cdot 6H_2O$	5.0 mg/l
KCl	8.0 mg/l

Trace elements as in starting medium

Administration of [14]*C*

During the first part of the experiment the algae are kept photosynthesizing in the light with a constant supply of 1.5 to 2 % unlabeled CO_2 in air for 0.5–1 h. Constant pH, temperature, and light intensity are maintained during this time, and during the subsequent exposure to [14]CO_2. In the experiments reported here the pH was kept at 6. Rate measurements of CO_2 uptake and O_2 evolution are made by making the closed system small, 435 ml for a few minutes, and observing the rate of change of CO_2 and O_2 tensions as indicated on the recorder. The closed gas system is made large again, and at zero time, [14]CO_2 is added to the system by turning a stopcock. At the same instant a solution of $NaH^{14}CO_3$ is injected directly into the algal suspension. The amount and specific radioactivity of the injected bicarbonate solution is so calculated that it will immediately bring the specific radioactivity of the dissolved CO_2 and bicarbonate already present in the algal suspension to its final value. This is the specific radioactivity which will obtain for all the CO_2 and bicarbonate in the gas and liquid phases of the closed system after complete equilibration has occurred. An example of this calculation is given in Table III. Samples of the algae suspension of uniform size are taken every 5 or 10 sec for the first few minutes, and then less frequently for periods up to 1 h. Each sample is taken directly into 4.0 ml of methanol (room temperature) in a centrifuge tube (preweighed). Sample tubes are reweighed to give the sample size ($\pm$ 1 %). After an hour at room temperature, the samples are centrifuged and the 80 % methanol extract removed. 1 ml of methanol is added to the residue and stirred a few minutes, then 4 ml water is added and the mixture

TABLE III

CALCULATION OF ^{12}C + ^{14}C FOR STEADY STATE EXPT. 18

	Volume	%CO$_2$	μmoles	μC^{14}C	Specific activity
A Gas phase at start	895	1.6	585	0	0
B ^{14}CO$_2$ loop	72		156	3767	
C Dissolved CO$_2$, HCO$_3$	125*		81.6		0
D NaH^{14}CO$_3$ injected			40.8	607.5	
Total	1092		863	4375	5.07 μC/μmole
C + D			122.4	607.5	4.95 μC/μmole

* Effective volume.

warmed at 60° for 10 min. After centrifugation and a further extraction with 1 ml of water, the combined clear extracts are concentrated at reduced pressure at below room temperature. The concentrated extract, or an aliquot portion thereof, is transferred quantitatively to the paper chromatogram and analyzed in two dimensions (phenol–water, butanol–propionic acid–water) as in earlier work[5]. The location of the radioactive compounds on the chromatograph is found by radioautography with X-ray film. When necessary, overlapping phosphate esters are eluted, treated with phosphatase and rechromatographed.

Determination of radioactivity in compounds

The amounts of radiocarbon in each compound of interest on the chromatograms from each sample is measured with a Geiger-Mueller tube. The paper chromatogram is placed on top of the radioautograph, which rests on a horizontal light table, so that the darkened areas of the film may be seen through the paper. The Geiger-Mueller tube has a Mylar window, gold-sputtered for conductivity, but transparent and thin (less than 1 mg/cm^2) to permit the passage of ^{14}C beta particles. This tube has an effective counting area of uniform sensitivity of about 17 cm^2. The top of the tube is transparent plastic so that paper and radioautograph may be viewed through the top of the tube. Thus the counting area of the tube may readily be placed in position over the radioactive compound on the paper. If the radioactive area is more than 4 cm across, or if it contains more than 20,000 counts/min (as counted by this tube on the paper), the radioactive area is divided into smaller areas which are counted one at a time (with the remainder of the spot covered by cards). The counting gas used is helium–isobutane (99:1). The counting voltage is about 1300 V. The sensitivity of the counter for ^{14}C beta particles in an infinitely thin layer on an aluminum planchet is about one count/3.1 disintegrations. However, only about one-third of the beta particles escape from the paper (Whatman No. 4) and the actual sensitivity of this tube for ^{14}C in compounds on the paper is about 1/11.2. These sensitivities were determined by comparison of counts from three aliquot portions of a known ^{14}C labeled solution: (a) chromatographed on paper, (b) dried on a planchet, and (c) placed in a scintillation counter with an internal standard. The radioactivity of each compound is counted on each side of the paper and an average is taken of the counts from the two sides. Comparison with determinations of radioactivity of compounds quantitatively eluted and placed on planchets indicates that this method of counting gives an accuracy of ± 5 %.

Rate measurements

Gas exchange: Measurements of the rates of CO_2 uptake, ^{14}C uptake and O_2 evolution by the photosynthesizing algae are made by taking the slopes of the three traces on the recorder. In order to obtain accurate readings in 10 min or less, the total effective gas volume of the closed circulating system is made small, about 435 ml. With 80 ml of 0.5 % algal suspension in the system the resulting change in O_2 or CO_2 pressure is about 0.5 % in 10 min in a typical experiment. This corresponds to a rate of 22 μmoles of gas exchange/min/ml of wet packed algae. The response of the Beckman Infrared Analyzer, model 15 A, used in these experiments is not completely linear in the range used (0 to 2.0 % CO_2) so that a correction based on a previously obtained calibration curve is applied to the CO_2 uptake curve plotted on the recorder. The response of the A. O. Beckman oxygen analyzer is essentially linear in the range used (19 to 21 %). The level of ^{14}C is plotted on the recorder as millivolts response of the Applied Physics Corpn.'s Vibrating Reed Electrometer to the ionization chamber (volume 118 ml, R = 10^9 ohms). From the known calibration of the ionization chamber this reading can be directly converted to μC of ^{14}C. From the $^{12}CO_2$ reading and the ^{14}C reading the specific radioactivity of the CO_2 may be calculated at all times during the experiment. This specific radioactivity is used to convert the rates of change of radioactivity in the system to rates of change of what we shall call "^{14}C" throughout this paper. For convenience of expression and calculation, this ^{14}C will be expressed in μmoles and represents the amount of ^{12}C and ^{14}C corresponding to a given measured amount of radioactivity in the CO_2 administered to the algae at any time during the experiment.

Total fixation in algae: In some experiments, small aliquot portions of each sample of algal material, taken and killed in alcohol during the course of the experiment, are spread in a thin layer on planchets with acetic acid, dried, and counted. The amount of ^{14}C found at each time of exposure of the algae to $^{14}CO_2$ is plotted and the slope of the curve drawn through these points gives the rate of appearance of ^{14}C in stable compounds in the plant.

Fixation of ^{14}C in compounds found on the paper chromatograph: After the ^{14}C in individual compounds found on the paper chromatogram has been measured, the amounts are sometimes totaled for each sample up to one minute, and a rate of appearance of ^{14}C in these compounds is calculated.

RESULTS

Steady state Expt. 18

The rates of exchange of gases before, during and at the end of the experiment are shown in Table IV. We shall take 15.5 μmoles/min as an average value for uptake of carbon during the experiment.

Aliquot portions of the samples were dried on planchets and their radioactivity was counted. When results of these counts were plotted *versus* time of sampling, the rate of fixation of ^{14}C into compounds stable to drying on the planchets was found to be about 15 μmoles/min (Fig. 3).

After chromatographic separation of the compounds, radioautographs, of which Fig. 4 is typical, were obtained. The radioactivity of each compound in each sample was determined and the total radiocarbon found in the various compounds

109

TABLE IV

RATES OF GAS EXCHANGE IN STEADY STATE EXPT. 18

All rates are given in μmoles/ml of wet packed algae.

	Carbon dioxide	14C*
Initial rate	17.9	
During experiment	16.6	15.1
Final rate	14.1	13.7

* See section *Methods of measurements of rate of gas exchange* for explanation of expression of 14C in μmoles. In theory the value for 14C and CO_2 should be the same. The difference is a reflection of inaccuracy in measurement of the slopes, especially CO_2.

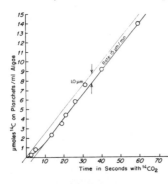

Fig. 3. Appearance of 14C in stable compounds (dried on planchets) in *Chlorella pyrenoidosa* vs. time of photosynthesis with 14CO_2.

Fig. 4. Radioautograph of chromatogram of *Chlorella pyrenoidosa* after 2 min photosynthesis with 14CO_2.

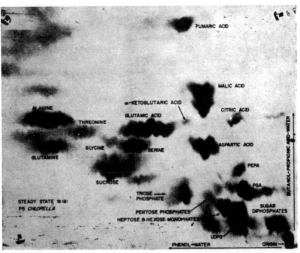

Fig. 4.

was plotted against time (Fig. 5). The maximum slope of the curve in Fig. 5 is 13 μmoles. This is a lower limit for the rate of appearance of ¹⁴C in soluble compounds which are also stable to chromatography. It does not take into account other compounds, too weakly radioactive to be counted, or "lost" from the front of our chromatograms. (In order to obtain good separation of phosphate esters we customarily allow the phenol–water solvent to drip from the ends of the chromatograms. Small amounts of labeled fatty material are lost in this way.)

After 30 sec, appreciable amounts of radioactivity are passing through the extractable precursor compounds seen on the chromatograms into non-extractable substances, which are not seen on the chromatograms. Consequently the rate of appearance of ¹⁴C in compounds on the paper decrease.

During the first ten seconds, the rate of appearance of ¹⁴C in stable compounds is less than the maximum rate during the subsequent time. This could be ascribed to mixing time of the added $H^{14}CO_3^-$ with the $H^{12}CO_3^-$ present initially, or alternately to the presence of an intermediate pool of either HCO_3^- or some other unstable or

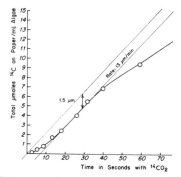

Fig. 5. Appearance of ¹⁴C in compounds on chromatograms prepared from *Chlorella pyrenoidosa* vs. time of photosynthesis with ¹⁴CO₂.

volatile compound. Such a compound would precede the stable soluble compounds in the fixation pathway. The size of this "pool", if it exists, cannot be greater than the difference between the fixation curve after 10 sec and a line of the maximum slope drawn through the origin (see Figs. 3 and 5). This is no more than 1.0 to 1.5 μmoles, which is equal to the carbon fixed in 4 to 6 sec in this experiment. A calculation of the amount of HCO_3^- which would be found inside algae cells in a volume of 1 ml with an internal pH of 7 in equilibrium with 1.7 % CO_2 gives a value of about 1 to 1.5 μmoles, depending on the volume available inside the cells. It seems to us to be not unreasonable to suppose that this "pool" is merely intracellular CO_2 and HCO_3^- but it does not matter to the subsequent argument whether it is this or some other unstable or volatile substance.

From the measured rates of uptake of CO_2 and ¹⁴C and from the rates of appearance of ¹⁴C in stable compounds these experimental findings may be listed: (a) The appearance of ¹⁴C in stable, nonvolatile compounds, after the first 10 sec of exposure of the plant to ¹⁴CO₂, is equal to the rate of total uptake of ¹⁴CO₂ within experimental error. (b) During the period between 10 and 30 sec exposure to $^{14}CO_2$, the appearance of ^{14}C in individual compounds which can be isolated by our methods of paper chromatography, is equal to at least 85 % of the rate of total uptake. (c) If there is a pool of CO_2, HCO_3^- or other unstable or volatile compound lying between administered CO_2 and stable compounds in the fixation pathway, its amount is not more than 1.0 to 1.5 μmoles (4 to 6 sec fixation) and it is essentially saturated after 10 sec.

Let us next consider the question of how much of this fixed ^{14}C must pass through the PGA pool.

In Fig. 6 are shown the labeling curves of some of the more rapidly labeled compounds and groups of compounds. By 3 min, compounds of the carbon reduction cycle are essentially saturated with radiocarbon. Secondary intermediates such as sucrose, malic acid, and several amino acids are not saturated until longer times (5 to 30 min). In order to evaluate the importance of the fixation pathway leading through PGA, we have tabulated the actual measurements of ^{14}C found in compounds

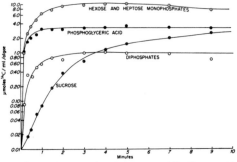

Fig. 6. Appearance of ^{14}C in PGA and sugar phosphates in *Chlorella pyrenoidosa* vs. time of photosynthesis with $^{14}CO_2$.

during the first minute (Table V). The ^{14}C found in all those compounds derived from PGA without further carboxylation (see Fig. 1) is added together (T_1). Compounds labeled by C_3–C_1 carboxylation are totaled separately (T_2). Since three of the carbon atoms in these compounds are derived from PGA, their total radioactivity is multiplied by a factor which is 3/4 times the degree of saturation of the PGA, which is presumed to be the same as that of their immediate precursor, namely, PEPA. (The saturation curves for PGA and PEPA are in fact very similar in this and other experiments.) The sum of T_1 and T_2f, representing measured ^{14}C derived from the primary reaction which forms PGA, is plotted in Fig. 7. Again the "pool" of HCO_3^- or other volatile or unstable compound is about 1 μmole and in this case it must precede PGA in the chain of reactions. Where one draws the curve of maximum slope through these points is somewhat arbitrary, but the maximum rate of appearance of ^{14}C in these compounds falls somewhere between 11 and 13 μmoles/min. Thus on the basis of the appearance of ^{14}C in these extractable, stable compounds alone, at least 70 to 85 % of all carbon fixed during photosynthesis (measured externally) is incorporated via the carbon reduction cycle. It must be emphasized

TABLE V

^{14}C (μMOLES/ML ALGAE) IN PHOTOSYNTHESIS INTERMEDIATES DURING FIRST MINUTE WITH $^{14}CO_2$

Steady State *Chlorella* 18.

Compound	Time in seconds of $^{14}CO_2$									Steady state value	
	2.5	5	8.5	13	18	26	31.5	40	59	μmoles carbon	μmoles compound
PGA	0.063	0.220	0.466	0.750	0.983	1.38	1.72	1.92	2.29	3.0	1.0
PEPA	0.0084	0.0083	0.026	0.041	0.047	0.093	0.114	0.132	0.170	0.2	0.07
Hexose monophosphate	0.017	0.063	0.205	0.429	0.677	1.14	1.60	1.99	2.73	5.5	0.9
Heptose monophosphate	0.011	0.027	0.080	0.157	0.247	0.406	0.617	0.766	0.955	1.8	0.26
Pentose monophosphate	0.0021	0.0096	0.011	0.024	0.035	0.054	0.074	0.067	0.133	? 0.2	? 0.04
Triose monophosphate	0.0069	0.0139	0.038	0.063	0.084	0.144	0.174	0.215	0.283	? 0.8	? 0.3
Diphosphates except ribulose	0.0041	0.013	0.026	0.044	0.053	0.093	0.138	0.160	0.203	0.54	—
Ribulose diphosphate	0.0045	0.0129	0.028	0.047	0.057	0.100	0.150	0.190	0.225	0.36	0.07
Alanine	—	0.025	0.024	0.049	0.075	0.170	0.257	0.397	0.869	? 15	? 5
Serine	—	0.015	0.012	0.016	0.013	0.027	0.039	0.053	0.120	1.2	? 0.4
Sucrose	—	—	—	—	0.0080	0.019	0.021	0.035	0.094	> 3.5	> 0.3
UDPG	—	—	—	0.0090	0.019	0.048	0.108	0.170	0.308	> 2.0	—
Total (T_1)	0.117	0.407	0.916	1.629	2.298	3.674	5.012	6.085	8.380		
Aspartic acid	—	—	0.0070	0.015	0.025	0.063	0.091	0.131	0.299	2.0	0.5
Fumaric acid	—	—	0.0020	0.0030	0.0080	0.013	0.025	0.050	0.091	0.7	0.18
Malic acid	—	0.0066	0.018	0.040	0.063	0.152	0.194	0.271	0.480	2.1	0.5
Total (T_2)	0.021	0.007	0.027	0.058	0.096	0.228	0.310	0.452	0.870		
x = PGA saturation	0.016	0.073	0.152	0.250	0.327	0.461	0.575	0.635	0.765		
f = 3x/4	—	0.055	0.116	0.158	0.246	0.347	0.432	0.476	0.574		
$T_2 \times f$	—	—	0.002	0.009	0.023	0.078	0.135	0.216	0.500		
Grand total $= T_1 + T_2f$	0.117	0.412	0.918	1.638	2.321	3.752	5.147	6.301	8.880		
$T_2 - T_2f$	—	—	0.025	0.049	0.073	0.150	0.175	0.236	0.370		

that this percentage is a lower limit based only on absolute measurements of identified compounds.

A lower limit for the amount of carbon incorporated via C_1 plus C_3 carboxylation is obtained by plotting T_2—T_2f (Fig. 7). The minimum rate of this incorporation is about 0.4 μmoles/min/ml algae, or about 3 % of the total. Note that this value is

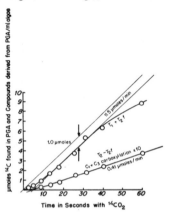

Fig. 7. Appearance of ^{14}C in compounds derived from PGA and in compounds derived from $C_1 + C_3$ carboxylation in *Chlorella pyrenoidosa vs.* time of photosynthesis with $^{14}CO_2$.

for the actual introduction of CO_2 and does not include the carbon derived from PGA (T_2f). The rate of incorporation of ^{14}C into these three compounds thus accounts for about 4 times 3, or 12 % of the total in this experiment. Other experiments indicate that the relative contribution of C_3–C_1 carboxylation varies considerably and tends to be higher (up to 3 times that reported in this case) when the rate of CO_2 fixation is greater and when amino acid synthesis is more rapid. In addition to the three compounds listed here, other substances may be derived in part from C_1–C_3 carboxylation, such as glutamic acid and citric acid, discussed below.

While at least 73 % of the total rate of fixation of carbon has thus been shown to be due to the carbon reduction cycle and C_1–C_3 addition, there is no indication of any other significant fixation pathway. In Fig. 8 the ^{14}C found in glutamic acid and in citric acid is shown. Could this labeling of glutamic acid be the result of a carboxylation of γ-aminobutyric acid? The maximum rate of labeling of glutamic acid and in citric acid is shown. The maximum rate of labeling of glutamic acid is about 0.7 μmoles/min or 4.5 % of all ^{14}C fixed. Since this rate is found between 5 and 20 min, it probably represents labeling of all five carbon atoms of glutamic acid, because the precursors are surely at least partially labeled after 5 min. The labeling due to carboxylation reaction would be expected to begin during the first 30 sec, if one is to judge by the other known carboxylation reactions which were discussed earlier. Yet, after the first 31.5 sec, the glutamic acid contains only 0.02 μmoles of ^{14}C. Between 40 and 60 sec, its labeling rate is only 0.2 μmoles/min. Moreover, γ-aminobutyric acid itself would have to be synthesized from CO_2 (by some as yet unknown route), if it were a precursor to glutamic acid, and would have to be appreciably labeled by the time glutamic acid reaches its maximum labeling rate. Yet ɯe can detect no radiocarbon in γ-aminobutyric acid in this experiment or in others ʃy this series, even after the algae have been exposed to $^{14}CO_2$ for 10 min. Clearly, ɯottle if any of the labeled glutamic acid formed in our experiments is made b

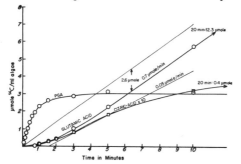

Fig. 8. Appearance of ^{14}C in PGA, glutamic acid and citric acid in *Chlorella pyrenoidosa vs.* time of photosynthesis with $^{14}CO_2$.

carboxylation of γ-aminobutyric acid. Rather, it must arise from other intermediate substances such as those formed by the two carboxylation mechanisms already discussed.

Note, however, that the rate of labeling of citric acid is by far too small to permit it to be the precursor of the labeled glutamic acid in any sequence such as:

$$\text{oxaloacetic acid} + \text{acetyl coenzyme A} \longrightarrow \text{citric acid} \rightarrow \rightarrow \rightarrow$$
$$\alpha\text{-oxoglutaric acid} + CO_2 \longrightarrow \text{glutamic acid}$$

Steady state Expt. 28

All the results described thus far were obtained in an experiment (steady state 18) in which the nutrient solution, though not automatically replenished, was sufficient to maintain the rate of photosynthesis at a nearly constant level during the course of the experiment. The results of steady state Expt. 28, in which the nutrient solution was replenished during the course of the experiment led to the same conclusions.

TABLE VI

COMPARISON OF STEADY STATE EXPERIMENTS 18 AND 28

Experiment	CO_2 uptake $\mu moles/min/ml$ algae	Rate of appearance of ^{14}C in compounds on chromatograms (20–40 sec)	RuDP saturation at 40 sec	PGA residual* carbon saturation according to	
				Reaction D	Reaction L
18	15.5	13	0.53	0.57	0.46
28	19.5	17–18	0.38	0.43	0.28

* See subsequent discussion for explanation of the term "residual". The degree of saturation at 40 sec is obtained by dividing the measured value of ^{14}C in the compound at 40 sec by the saturation level of ^{14}C in the compound (or residual atoms) after 10 min exposure of the algae to $^{14}CO_2$.

115

These results are summarized and compared with steady state Expt. 18 in Table VI. Though not shown in the table, the maximum rate of appearance of ^{14}C in observable compounds derived from the carboxylation reaction leading to PGA (the carbon reduction cycle) was 70 to 90 % of the externally measured rate of ^{14}C uptake.

DISCUSSION

When CALVIN AND MASSINI[13] reported the formation of PGA in an overall reaction requiring ribulose diphosphate and CO_2 they proposed that the reaction in the light gave one molecule of PGA and one of triose phosphate but in the dark gave two molecules of PGA. WILSON[14] discussed this possibility further after it was realized that the carboxylation did not involve an intermediate splitting of the ribulose to triose and diose. The dark reaction in whole plants[15] and the reaction in isolated enzyme systems[16, 17] was found to give rise to two PGA molecules. Also, it is clear from previous kinetic studies[1, 18] of carbon fixation during photosynthesis that the ^{14}C entering the carbon reduction cycle via the ribulose carboxylation passes through the carboxyl group of PGA initially. This is consistent with the fact, established for the isolated enzyme system by HORECKER[16], that the CO_2 is bonded to the number two carbon atom of ribulose diphosphate. More recently PARK[19] has shown by means of inhibition studies in broken spinach chloroplasts that ^{14}C entering that system must pass through PGA. That is, PGA is a biochemical intermediate compound—not merely a compound formed by thermal breakdown after the plant is killed.

We shall present here an argument, based on kinetic data, which indicates that the carboxylation of RuDP in vivo during photosynthesis gives rise to only one molecule of 3-PGA.

If the ^{14}C which has just entered PGA from $^{14}CO_2$ is subtracted from the total ^{14}C in PGA, the ^{14}C in the remaining carbon atoms of the PGA must all be derived from ribulose diphosphate.

Let us consider the two reactions:

The position of the ^{14}C which has just entered the cycle as $^{14}CO_2$ is indicated by the asterisks. In reaction D, there are five remaining carbon atoms of PGA (numbers 1 to 5) which must be derived from RuDP, while in reaction L there are two such "residual" carbon atoms (numbers 1 and 2). The steady state concentration of PGA in steady state Expt. 18 is 3.0 μmoles of carbon/ml algae, hence the carboxyl carbon concentration is 1.0 μmole of carbon. However, if reaction D is correct, only one-half

116

of this carboxyl carbon, or 0.5 μmole, is derived immediately from CO_2; the other half (carbon atom 3) comes from RuDP. We shall subtract the ^{14}C due to newly incorporated $^{14}CO_2$ from the total ^{14}C found in PGA at each time and for each of these two cases. The specific radioactivity of the remainder may then be compared with the specific radioactivity of the RuDP from which it must be derived.

In order to make this subtraction it is necessary first to calculate the radiocarbon in the carboxyl group of PGA as a function of the time of exposure of the algae to $^{14}CO_2$. This calculation requires in turn a calculation of the saturation curve of the "CO_2 pool", although this could be assumed to be saturated from the beginning without seriously affecting the results.

Consider the steady state system:

$$CO_2 \xrightarrow{R} \text{Pool 1} \xrightarrow{R} \text{Pool 2} \longrightarrow \text{etc.}$$

Let C_1 and C_2 be the steady state concentrations of Pools 1 and 2 and let x and y be the degrees of saturation with ^{14}C of these pools (respectively) as a function of time of exposure of the algae to $^{14}CO_2$. R is the rate of flow of carbon into the system and through the two pools. It is also assumed in this case that the rates of the back reactions are negligible compared to the rates of the forward reactions.

For a small increment of time, the change in degree of saturation is the difference between the rate of flow of ^{14}C into the pool (R) and the rate of flow of carbon out of the pool (Rx), divided by the size of the pool C_1; $dx/dt = (R - Rx)/C_1$. Integration and determination of the integration constant at $t = 0$ gives $x = 1 - \text{expt}(-R/C_1)t$.

During a small increment of time, the change in degree of saturation of the second pool is the difference between the rate of flow of ^{14}C into the second pool (Rx) and the rate of flow out (Ry) divided by the pool size C_2;

$$y = \frac{Rx - Ry}{C_2} = \frac{R}{C_2}[1 - \exp(-Rt/C_1) - y]$$

Integration and determination of constants at $t = 0$ leads to two solutions, one for the case $C_1 \neq C_2$:

$$y = 1 - \left(\frac{C_1}{C_1 - C_2}\right)\exp(-Rt/C_1) + \left(\frac{C_2}{C_1 - C_2}\right)\exp(-Rt/C_2)$$

and another for the case $C_1 = C_2$:

$$y = 1 - (1 - Rt/C)\exp(-Rt/C)$$

In applying these equations to the data from steady state Expt. 18 we have assumed a value of $C_1 = 1.2$ μmoles for the "CO_2 pool" (Fig. 1) and a value of 0.2 μmoles/sec ($= 12$ μmoles/min) for R. The resulting values for x are shown by curve A, Fig. 9.

If reaction D is correct, the PGA carboxyl pool arising from newly incorporated CO_2 is 0.5 μmoles and its degree of saturation y is given by curve B, Fig. 9. If reaction L is correct, this pool is 1.0 μmole and the saturation curve y is that shown as curve C. Curve B times 0.5 and curve C times 1.0 give, as a function of time, the respective μmoles of ^{14}C in the PGA carboxyl pool derived directly from CO_2.

The degree of saturation of the residual carbon atoms of PGA (those which are derived from RuDP) may now be calculated by subtracting from the experimentally determined [^{14}C]PGA these values of the CO_2-derived carboxyl (0.5 B for reaction D, 1.0 C for reaction L) and dividing by the pool sizes of the residual carbons (2.5 and

2.0 respectively). The resulting saturation curves are shown in Fig. 10. In the same figure, Curve R is the saturation curve for ribulose diphosphate, obtained by dividing the experimentally determined ^{14}C labeling of RuDP by its steady state concentration, which was 0.36 μmoles/ml algae.

If the carboxylation of RuDP were to lead to the formation of two molecules of PGA (reaction D), then all of the carbon atoms of RuDP must give rise to the "residual" carbon atoms of PGA. The degree of saturation of these residual carbon atoms at no time could exceed the degree of saturation of the carbon atoms of RuDP. Since the calculated values for these residual atoms, (PGA-0.5 B)/2.5, do exceed those of RuDP at all times after 12 sec, reaction D does not appear to be correct. The curve for reaction L does not exceed the saturation of RuDP until about 1 min. In this case, the residual carbon atoms of PGA are derived only from carbon atoms 2 and 3 of RuDP, and thus may exceed the saturation of the average of carbon atoms

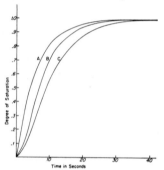

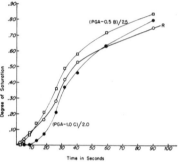

Fig. 9. Degree of saturation (vs. time of photosynthesis with $^{14}CO_2$) of "CO_2 pool" and of PGA carboxyl derived immediately from $^{14}CO_2$ according to two proposed carboxylation reactions. Curve A is for "CO_2 pool", curve B is for PGA carboxyl derived immediately from $^{14}CO_2$ according to reaction D, curve C is for PGA carboxyl according to reaction L.

Fig. 10. Degree of saturation of ribulose diphosphate (R) vs. time of photosynthesis with $^{14}CO_2$ compared with degrees of saturation of residual carbon atoms of PGA according to two proposed carboxylation reactions.

1, 2, 3, 4, and 5 of RuDP. In fact, this is not surprising, since earlier degradation studies on RuDP[1] showed that, during ^{14}C incorporation in photosynthesis, carbon atom 3 is first labeled, followed by carbon atoms 1 and 2, followed finally by carbon atoms 4 and 5. The saturation curve for the residual PGA carbon atoms according to reaction L is thus about as would be expected.

Note that after 30 sec the carboxyl carbon of PGA would be saturated and the same conclusion could be reached by looking only at the curves from 30 to 90 sec, which are not dependent on the foregoing calculations of CO_2 pool and PGA carboxyl saturation. At these longer times it is sufficient to plot simply the curves for (PGA-0.5)/2.5, (PGA-1.0)/2.0, and RuDP/0.32 all as a function of time.

We conclude, therefore, that the labeling curves for PGA and RuDP in this experiment can best be interpreted as resulting from the occurrence of reaction L. That is, the *in vivo* carboxylation reaction of the carbon reduction cycle during

118

photosynthesis appears to produce one molecule of PGA and one molecule of some other three carbon compound.

Steady state Expt. 28 gave very similar results, from 10 sec to saturation (see Table VI for comparison at 40 sec).

From these experiments alone we cannot identify this three carbon compound. It could be merely a small pool of PGA itself, tightly bound to an enzyme, or in some other way kept apart from the principal PGA pool. Such a pool of PGA molecules, if sufficiently small ($>$ 0.1 μmole), would not be distinguishable from the other PGA pool by our methods.

Alternatively, the six carbon product of the carboxylation reaction may be reductively split to one molecule of 3-PGA and one molecule of triose phosphate. In either case, the requirement for the reaction leading to PGA and triose phosphate must be light (or cofactors derived from the light reaction), and the intact chloroplast, or some intact sub-unit of the chloroplast, as it occurs naturally in the living cell.

One cannot say at the present time whether or not any of the chloroplasts or chloroplast fragments isolated from broken cells retain the capacity to carry out such a reductive splitting of the six carbon intermediate of the carbon reduction cycle. In such cell-free systems, the carbon reduction cycle may well operate only via the carboxylation reaction leading to two molecules of free 3-PGA. Recently PARK[20] has prepared electron micrographs of chloroplast and chloroplast fragments which had been found by him to have about as high a rate of photosynthetic CO_2 reduction as any such rates reported for cell-free systems. When compared with electron micrographs of chloroplasts in intact cells, these isolated fragments appear to have undergone considerable physical change, particularly in regard to the apparent density of the stroma and spacing between lamellae. It is possible that the reductive carboxylation pathway, if correct, operates only in the unaltered lamellar system by means of some rather direct transfer of photochemically-produced reducing power from the pigmented layer to the carbon reduction cycle.

If two different three carbon compounds are formed *in vivo* in the light by the carboxylation of RuDP, and if these two products are kept separate until they have been converted to triose phosphate, and react with each other to give hexose, then the resulting hexose molecule might be dissimilarly labeled in its two halves, nameyl carbon atoms 1, 2, and 3, and carbon atoms 4, 5, and 6. Such asymmetry has been reported by GIBBS AND KANDLER[21, 22]. However, other explanations of the phenomenon are also consistent with the carbon reduction cycle[3].

ACKNOWLEDGEMENT

The work described in this paper was sponsored by the United States Atomic Energy Commission, University of California, Berkeley, Calif. (U.S.A.).

REFERENCES

[1] J. A. BASSHAM, A. A. BENSON, L. D. KAY, A. Z. HARRIS, A. T. WILSON AND M. CALVIN, *J. Am. Chem. Soc.*, 76 (1954) 1760.
[2] M. CALVIN, *J. Chem. Soc.*, (1956) 1895.
[3] J. A. BASSHAM AND M. CALVIN, *The Path of Carbon in Photosynthesis*, Prentice-Hall, Englewood Cliffs, New Jersey, 1957.

[4] M. CALVIN AND A. A. BENSON, Science, 109 (1949) 140.
[5] A. A. BENSON, J. A. BASSHAM, M. CALVIN, T. C. GOODALE, V. A. HAAS AND W. STEPKA, J. Am. Chem. Soc., 72 (1950) 1710.
[6] A. A. BENSON, Arch. Biochem. Biophys., 32 (1951) 223.
[7] A. A. BENSON, J. Am. Chem. Soc., 73 (1951) 2971.
[8] A. A. BENSON, J. A. BASSHAM, M. CALVIN, A. G. HALL, H. E. HIRSH, S. KAWAGUCHI, V. LYNCH AND N. E. TOLBERT, J. Biol. Chem., 196 (1952) 703.
[9] M. GOODMAN, D. F. BRADLEY AND M. CALVIN, J. Am. Chem. Soc., 75 (1953) 1962.
[10] M. GOODMAN, A. A. BENSON AND M. CALVIN, J. Am. Chem. Soc., 77 (1955) 4257.
[11] O. WARBURG, Science, 128 (1958) 68.
[12] R. W. KRAUSS, in J. S. BURLEW, Algal Culture from Laboratory to Pilot Plant, Carnegie Institution of Washington Publication 600, Washington D.C., 1953, p. 94.
[13] M. CALVIN AND P. MASSINI, Experientia, 8 (1952) 445.
[14] A. T. WILSON AND M. CALVIN, J. Am. Chem. Soc., 77 (1955) 5948.
[15] J. A. BASSHAM, K. SHIBATA, K. STEENBERG, J. BOURDON AND M. CALVIN, J. Am. Chem. Soc., 78 (1956) 4120.
[16] A. WEISSBACH, B. L. HORECKER AND J. HURWITZ, J. Biol. Chem., 218 (1956) 795.
[17] W. B. JAKOBY, D. O. BRUMMOND AND S. OCHOA, J. Biol. Chem., 218 (1956) 811.
[18] A. A. BENSON, S. KAWAGUCHI, P. M. HAYES AND M. CALVIN, J. Am. Chem. Soc., 74 (1952) 4477.
[19] R. B. PARK, N. G. PON, K. P. LOUWRIER AND M. CALVIN, Biochim. Biophys. Acta, 42 (1960) 27.
[20] R. B. PARK, Annual Winter Meeting, The Western Society of Naturalists, Los Angeles, University of Southern California, December 1959.
[21] M. GIBBS AND O. KANDLER, Plant Physiol., 31 (1956) 411.
[22] M. GIBBS AND O. KANDLER, Proc. Natl. Acad. Sci. U.S., 43 (1957) 446.

Biochim. Biophys. Acta, 43 (1960) 447–464

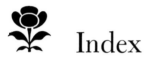 Index

 Index